Contents

Introduction 6

Whole Class Games

Whole Class Games: Introduction 11

Spare Minute Algebra 1 12

Spare Minute Algebra 2 13

Match the Answer Rules 14

Match the Answer Expression Sheet 15

The Answer's $10x + 7$ 16

An 'I like' session 17

'I like' Algebraic Expressions 1 18

'I like' Algebraic Expressions 2 19

Fix the Machine 20

Guess my Point 21

Loop Games

Loop Games: Introduction 23

Loop Games Rules 1 24

Loop Games Rules 2 25

Add and Subtract x. Game 1 26

Add and Subtract x. Game 2 28

Function Loops 30

Harder Function Loops 32

Loopy Powers 1 34

Loopy Powers 2 36

Quadratic Add and Subtract 38

Easier What Went In? 40

What Went In? 42

Quadratic Loop Game A 44

Quadratic Loop Game B 47

Contents (cont.)

Four in a Line

Four in a Line: Introduction 49

Four in a Line Rules 50

Addition and Subtraction Four in a Line 51

Substitution Four in a Line 52

Three in a Line Rules 53

Three in a Line Board 54

Multiplication and Division Four in a Line 55

Quadratic Four in a Line 56

Target Games

Target Games: Introduction 57

Linear Targets 59

Easier Targets 62

Negative Targets 65

Quadratic Targets 68

Equation Card Games

Equation Card Games: Introduction 71

Equation Card Games Rules 72

Simple Equation Game Solutions 1 to 8 73

Equation Game – Variable Letters 75

Hard Equation Game Solutions 0 to 9 77

Equation Cards – Negative Solutions –1 to –6 79

Two Sided Equations 81

Equation Cards Fractional Solutions 83

Quadratic Equation Game Roots 1 to 6 85

Quadratic Equation Game Roots ±1 to ±6 86

Simultaneous Equation Games

Simultaneous Equation Games: Introduction 89

Simultaneous Equation Games Rules 88

Match and Solve 1 91

Match and Solve 2 92

Match and Solve 3 93

Match and Solve 4 94

Sequence Games

Sequence Games: Introduction 95

Create a Sequence 96

Grab the Formula 97

Sequence Loops 98

The Longest Sequence 100

Assorted Games

Assorted Games: Introduction 101

Running Total 102

Substitution Bingo 103

Expressions for Bingo 104

The Yin Yang Game 105

Quadratic Dominoes Rules 106

Quadratic Dominoes 107

Introduction

The games in this book were developed while I was researching the use of games in algebra in schools, and I was amazed that so little justification existed for their use. The assumption seems to be that games are fun and so they are a good thing to do. Setting up games in the classroom is time consuming in terms of preparation of equipment and demanding from an organisation point of view. Also, in some ways, it leads to a loss of teacher control of pupil learning, as well as the loss of the volume of recorded pupil activity produced by more formal activities. I felt therefore that a deeper analysis of what goes on when games are used as a pedagogic device was needed. Over three years I spent many hours watching groups of children playing games and tried to perceive the kind of learning opportunities there were. This set of games were largely invented, often with the help of the pupils, during this time.

I observed many interesting outcomes of playing games, some of them were fairly obvious, but others only struck me as time went on. I believe it is important to look at these because it is only too easy for critics to say that playing a game is not doing proper mathematics and that there is no record of what the pupils have done. The latter can to some extent be overcome, if overcome it must be, by asking the pupils to write about what they did while playing the game.

The outcomes of this work are divided into three categories; learning, ways of working and pupil experience.

Learning

- **A game can generate an unreasonable amount of practice.**
  By unreasonable I mean that the pupils carry out far more 'computations' than they would be expected to do or ever manage to get through if they were faced with a conventional textbook exercise. This happens partly because they are working mentally but also because their attention is on carrying out a 'move' in the game and not on how much work they are having to do. It seems to give a sense of purpose to what is being worked out.

- **Algebraic games create a meaning for algebraic symbolism.**
  Throughout my work in school I was astonished by the complex notation that pupils were able to handle in the context of a game. The suppression of the multiplication sign caused the normal problems, but once this was overcome, even average ability pupils were able to handle complex expressions in several contexts including simplification, equations, formulae and functions. Also, I felt confident that they all were clear that a letter stood for a number and that the value of an expression varied with the number which was input to it.

- **A game will often result in the making of generalised statements.**
  Not all games have this potential, but many do. Good examples of this are the target games, the Yin-Yang game and the 'I like' games in this collection. In each case the players are likely to make statements such as: 'this will always give a positive result'; 'this expression will always be a multiple of 3 for this dice'.

A game can act as a concept developer.
During my work it was clear that almost all the pupils were able to develop strategies for solving equations. Equations which could be solved by inverse operations seemed rapidly to acquire a method of solution which was perhaps not algebraically formal, but was based on a full understanding of what was going on.

For example: $\dfrac{24}{x + 2} = 4$

led to $x + 2 = 6$ and even had x been replaced by x^2, the equation would have been solved with the same ease. This was certainly true for the Year 8 pupils with whom I worked, who had, at that time, done almost no algebraic work. Older and more able pupils were able to develop strategies for solving $7x = 5x + 10$ and for simultaneous equations.

A game can allow the introduction of ideas which are difficult to develop in other ways.
There was a point in my explorations when I wondered whether the problems the pupils were having with e.g. $2x$ was due to the fact that they thought the rule changed when the letter changed. I therefore set up a sorting game which consisted of a set of cards all of which had a simple linear equation on them, but the set contained 4 copies of each equation using a different letter. I asked the group to sort them by their solutions. Soon there were protests of 'I've just solved this one' and when I asked what they meant they responded that it was the same equation with a different letter. Strangely, to my mind, they didn't then just sort them by the particular equation, but continued to solve them numerically. At the end some mistakes had been made and there were not 4 cards in each set. I explained that there should be 4 in each set and after a short time one of them said "I know – its the equations that are the same that should be in the same pile". I do not know quite how, in a formal setting, I could have worked quite so directly on the idea that the letter used in an equation makes no difference to the solution. I do not believe that putting two of these equations together in an exercise would be at all the same. The target games also led to all kinds of subtle knowledge about what values a formula could give. I found it very surprising that they had to learn that in a dice game you could only get a non-integer if there was a division!

Games seem to be able to lead pupils to work above their normal level.
A game does not define the academic limits of the work in any way and since there is a natural wish to win, pupils will often devise ways of looking at the work they are doing which lead them way beyond what they are expected to achieve. Examples of this are the complexity of equation which Year 8 learned to handle, the way in which pupils playing linear targets married an awareness of the properties of their formula with probability and started to talk about the probability of winning. I was amazed too by a Year 9 boy who spontaneously put bounds on the values

his formula could take when playing Negative Targets. A game appears to free the pupils from feeling a need to do something which the teacher wants and expects, thus allowing them to think freely about the situation

Ways of working

A game leads pupils to talk mathematics.
I cannot prove that this is important but I came to believe that the activity of reading equations and formulae 'out aloud' was of value to pupils in getting more accustomed to these strange objects. One does not normally read equations out loud if they are in an exercise! This was helped considerably by asking pairs of pupils to work together as a single player. This I would also strongly recommend because...

A game can create discussion of all kinds.
This is greatly enhanced by the pairing technique described above, because the partners have to verbalise their ideas about the next move to each other and justify their opinions. This not only helps them, but can be very informative for a passing teacher who can eavesdrop and assess where they have got to in their thinking. Co-operative games can be very useful in creating discussion too. There is always a lot of discussion if a set of cards (twelve or eighteen of them) are chosen from a loop game and the pupils are asked, as a puzzle, to make the cards into one large loop.

Games put pressure on players to work mentally.
This is obvious in many ways but I did not think about it in the context of algebra until one of the Year 8 girls reported, in response to a simple questionnaire, that I had been doing 'mental algebra' with them. It may be that it is just as important to work mentally in algebra before getting used to presenting work in more formal ways. I believe that it helps pupils to continue to think about what they are doing rather than just applying memorised routines.

A game does not define the way in which a problem is to be solved or worked out.
For example when an equation card game is first played the pupils are not given any method for solving the equations. They develop their own. In the same way a target game does not, of itself, suggest how players should decide whether to change their formula card or not. They must devise strategies for making this decision..

A game often can be played at more then one level.
As a result of the previous property of games, it is possible for the players to play the game with more or less skill or perception depending on their own competence. They will often learn to develop their level of play by watching and listening to the other players. Equation card games are a good example of this where a simple substitution strategy can be used until a better one is developed.

Pupil experience

This last set of outcomes were the ones of which I only gradually became aware and which I see as of particular interest because so many of them are concerned with the players' feelings about what is happening.

It is acceptable to learn the rules of a game gradually.
No-one expects to be able to learn all the rules of a game at once. Pupils do not seem to distinguish between the procedural rules and the mathematical rules. This allows pupils to query the mathematical rules without loss of face. For example, it freed them to continue to query the meaning of $2x$ until they felt confident about it.

Games are played in a context in which there is usually unthreatening help available.
When a game is played by pairs then a pupil's partner is always there to help make decisions about what to do or to explain something which her partner does not understand. In addition, in most groups, other players will make suggestions if a player is stuck, if only to keep the game moving on. This is one of the reasons for playing with each player's cards exposed in a loop game, so that a loop is not broken by a player failing to recognise a card which can be played.

The pieces used in a game are concrete objects.
When a pupil is faced by a set of examples to work he feels pressure to answer them in the given order and there is a sense of failure if one proves too hard. Very often, in a game, there is a choice of which 'piece' one uses. In target games one can change a target card if the formula looks threatening. In loop games I have heard pairs, when there was a choice of which card to play, decide to play the one which they found most threatening to get rid of it. At the end of an equation card game I have seen pupils offer an equation which they could not solve to someone else to solve and so to win the card. I have had cards held out to me for help - much more expressive than pointing to a problem on a page! I have even found cards under the table and wondered whether they had been dropped to get rid of them! There are perhaps implications here about setting formal exercises which do not have numbers and are scattered randomly on the page and inviting the pupils to solve them in the order that they prefer. Or even perhaps presenting problems on a set of cards, but that would be hard to organise!

A game allows a pupil to hide until he feels confident.
In watching groups of pupils playing games I noticed that there were those who played quietly and rather mechanically for a while and then suddenly started to join in and make suggestions. It seemed that in a game situation they had the freedom to assess the situation without pressure until they felt they had things sorted out and then to contribute in a more positive fashion.

Clearly there are other types of activity which produce many of these outcomes, only some of them are in any way unique to the game playing situation.

However what seems clear to me is that games are a way of reducing teacher domination and control of the situation in a way which has positive outcomes for the learners.

Introducing games in the classroom

If a game is to be played by the whole class at the same time, working in groups of 6 or so, then clearly some thought has to be given to how the pupils are taught the rules and procedures of the game. What follows here are some thoughts about how to make this as efficient as possible.

It will be noted that the games in this booklet are largely organised by type of game. The re-use of different types of game for different mathematical purposes simplifies their introduction greatly as the class have only to be told that it is a target game or a loop game and they know how to play it. At most it may be necessary to look at the particular type of card or dice to be used.

In teaching games to large groups I have found three different methods that work well depending on the game and the situation:

- Introduce the game to one group of pupils while the others are completing some individual work and then divide the whole class into groups, putting one of the first group into each group to teach them the game.

- Play the game with the class divided into the groups in which they will subsequently play and play the game with the whole class, each group acting as a single player.

- Choose a set of pupils to come to the front of the class and play the game as a demonstration, possibly with assistance in decision making from the whole class. If this is done it may be useful to have large-size cards which can be seen by the whole class. I have used this technique a lot when introducing the more complex loop games, by asking the players to get the set of cards which I give them into a single loop. For other games it can be useful to have cards made from OHT film cut up so that these can be projected.

The use of pairs working as a single player has already been discussed as a way of encouraging discussion and indeed concept development. It has other advantages in that a larger number of pupils can use the same set of materials, so that there are fewer groups in the classroom to set-up and manage and fewer materials to produce and store!

Storage is inevitably a problem and I found myself losing and remaking sets of games until I adopted the system of keeping a class set of any particular game in a plastic box clearly marked with its name! Plastic bags of games do not work at all well. If the pupils can manage the size of card shown in this book, then it is quite easy to store class sets in a small box. I found that they were big enough, but the cards can, of course, be enlarged if this is felt desirable.

Whole Class Games

Introduction

These games are specifically designed to be played with the whole class. They therefore have a role to play as starters or as worthwhile activities to fill spare minutes at the end of a lesson.

Some of them can also be used by groups of children once the game is well understood but this is not their main purpose. The idea of them is distinct from the use of the whole class situation to act out a new game as is described in the introduction to this booklet.

Spare Minute Algebra 1

The teacher announces a target for the round. This can be chosen from the following list or similar ones:

- Greater than 25
- Less than 64
- Between 16 & 40
- Odd number between 25 & 40
- Even number greater than 80
- Multiple of 3
- Multiple of 7 greater than 50
- Prime number
- Square number
- Triangular number
- Cube number
- Factor of 96

Each player (could be a pair) writes down an expression of the form $ax + b$.

To start with a and b are positive integers, later they can be non-zero integers.

The teacher rolls a dice, of any type as chosen, and tells the students the score obtained, which is the value for x. Students then substitute this value into their expressions.

The player or players meeting the target score a point.

The players may change the formula they use for each target.

Spare Minute Algebra 2

The teacher needs a dice of any type e.g. 1 to 6, 0 to 9, 1 to 10.

Ask each player to write down 6 expressions of the form $ax + b$, where a and b are positive integers. The teacher says, 'Cross out an expression which will always be ☐ if I throw this dice.' The box should be filled with one of the examples listed below or similar targets.

- Even
- Odd
- Multiple of 3
- Multiple of 5
- Multiple of 10
- Bigger than 4
- Smaller than 4
- Not prime

For example if the target is 'not prime' a player could cross out $2x + 4$.

If the target is 'bigger than 4' a player could cross out $x + 4$ provided the dice used does not have zero on it.

Each player crosses out one expression in the category if they have one.

This is repeated for different targets.

The first player to cross out all his expressions wins.

ALTERNATIVE VERSION

The last player to be left with expressions in his list wins.

Match the Answer Rules

AS A CLASS ACTIVITY

Arrange the class into groups of about four. Number the groups from 1 to whatever. Give each group a copy of the expressions sheet.

Ask group 1 to choose an expression. Write e.g. $2x - 1$ = on the board
Throw a 0 to 9 dice.

Allow about a minute for each group to look for a second expression which gives the same answer for the dice throw.

Ask group 1 first for their answer

e.g. for a throw of 1 the group could suggest $4x - 3$

Write the complete equation on the board

$$2x - 1 = 4x - 3$$

$$x = 1$$

The group then scores a point.

Go round the groups in order. Each group scores a point for an answer which has not been used before.

If no group can find a suitable expression then group 1 can win a point for suggesting something that would work but which is not on the sheet.

For example if the dice throw were 9 they could suggest $3x - 10$.

Repeat the process starting with each group in turn.

AS A GROUP ACTIVITY

Once the game is understood it can be played in the same way by a group. They will need some kind of timing device for the thinking time.

Match the Answer Expression Sheet

Match the Answer Expression Sheet

$2x - 1$

AIM

Match the Answer Expression Sheet

$3x - 2$

AIM

Match the Answer Expression Sheet

$12 - 2x$

AIM

Match the Answer Expression Sheet

$8 - x$

AIM

Match the Answer Expression Sheet

$15 - 3x$

AIM

Match the Answer Expression Sheet

$2x + 1$

AIM

Match the Answer Expression Sheet

$2x + 2$

AIM

Match the Answer Expression Sheet

$3x + 1$

AIM

Match the Answer Expression Sheet

$3x + 2$

AIM

Match the Answer Expression Sheet

$3x - 1$

AIM

Match the Answer Expression Sheet

$16 - 3x$

AIM

Match the Answer Expression Sheet

$6 - x$

AIM

Match the Answer Expression Sheet

$4x - 4$

AIM

Match the Answer Expression Sheet

$4x - 3$

AIM

Match the Answer Expression Sheet

$2x + 3$

AIM

Match the Answer Expression Sheet

$14 - 2x$

AIM

Match the Answer Expression Sheet

$2 + x$

AIM

Match the Answer Expression Sheet

$3 + x$

AIM

The answer's $10x + 7$

A WHOLE CLASS GAME

Put this expression (or any other chosen one) on the board.

Invite the 'players' in turn to offer a 'sum' to which this is the answer.

Here 'players' may mean individuals, pairs, tables or halves of the class as seems best.

Score as follows:

$10x + 8 - 1$ scores 4 points

$10x + 9 - 2$ scores 3 points

$10x + 10 - 3$ scores 2 points

Any subsequent expressions of the same form score one point only

It is up to the teacher to decide whether $10x + 5 + 2$ is a new form or not. The teacher may choose to ask the class to suggest what a particular question is going to score, since this will help pupils to look at algebraic shape.

Expressions such as $11x - x + 7$ or $2(5x + 4) - 1$ would clearly be a new form and go back to scoring 4 points.

Once a class has understood the principle of the game it can also be played as a group game with the teacher acting as referee in cases of disagreement.

An 'I like' Session

Choose to use Sheet 1 or Sheet 2

Pupils are given the sheet or the sheet is projected using an OHP. The teacher (or pupil) starts off the session by saying "I like number 4." Individuals in the class ask for example "Do you like number 21?", etc.

If the teacher's rule is 'The answer is always even', she will say 'I hate 21', but would agree that she likes 16, if asked.

When pupils are confident that they know the rule they have to write it down and say which expressions on the sheet belong to it (and possibly devise a few more expressions which fit it).

POSSIBLE RULES

Algebra expressions 1:

Always even; always odd; could give negative answers; always positive etc.

Algebra expressions 2:

Always even; always odd; could give negative answers; always positive; must be bigger than 5 etc.

'I Like' Algebraic Expressions 1

1. $a + b$

2. $a + 3b$

3. $2a + b$

4. $2(a + b)$

5. $a - b$

6. $a - 3b$

7. $3(a - b)$

8. $a + b + c$

9. $2a + 3b + 4c$

10. $5a - 2c$

11. $2a + 4b$

12. $6b - 2a$

13. $4a + b$

14. $2(2a + b)$

15. $5ab + c$

16. $2ac$

17. $4a + 2ab$

18. $6b - c$

19. $4b + a$

20. $3b + 5c$

21. $3(2a + 5b)$

22. $2(a + b)$

23. $6(b - a)$

24. $3a + 2c$

25. $5ac + b$

26. $2a + 4c$

27. $3(a + 2b)$

28. $6(3 + a)$

29. $\dfrac{a}{4}$

30. $\dfrac{a}{2} + 1$

31. $2a + 1$

32. $4a - 1$

33. $3a - 1$

'I Like' Algebraic Expressions 2

1. $a^2 + b^2$

2. ab^2

3. $a(a + c)$

4. a^2c

5. a^2b^2

6. $a^2 + b^2$

7. $2a^3$

8. ab^2

9. $4a^2b$

10. $5ab^2$

11. $a^2 + b^3$

12. $a^2 - b^3$

13. $3(a^2 + b)$

14. $5(2a^2 + c)$

15. $a^2 + 2b$

16. $a + 2b^2$

17. $a^3 + b^2$

18. $3a^2$

19. a^2bc

20. $a^2 + 1$

21. $b^2 + a^2 + 1$

22. $2a(b + 1)$

23. $4a^2 + 2b^2$

24. ab^2

Fix the Machine

Tell the class that you are thinking of a number machine. When 1 goes in 2 comes out.

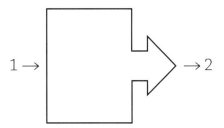

Tell them that they will score one point for any (algebraic) machine that satisfies this, but that the person who gets the largest output, when 3 is the input, will get 2 points.

Allow a thinking time, which could be timed with a timing device. Then ask the pairs in turn to say what their machine is. The rest of the class must decide to accept or not accept the machine.

Repeat this as many times as required with different input numbers and different targets for the second input number, e.g. smallest, nearest to zero, negative, a multiple of 5, a prime number.

As a variant the scoring could be:
- One point for a machine that satisfies the first requirement.
- A bonus point for a machine which no-one else suggests.

So in the above example the label $x + 1$ might score 1, but perhaps $x^3 + 1$ might score 2 points. The person(s) meeting the target score one point on top of the above.

In this case pupils might be allowed to write down several possible machines and suggest the most advantageous one when answers are given round the class. If this is allowed the pair who give an answer first should change at each round.

Guess my Point

THIS CAN BE PLAYED WITH A WHOLE CLASS OR BY A GROUP OF PUPILS.

Each player will need a sheet of square dotty paper, with axes drawn in the centre. Ordinary squared paper can also be used, but if so it must be made clear that it is the grid points only which are being selected.

The teacher (or later one of the players) chooses secretly one of the points on the sheet.

Players in turn ask a question which will have a yes/no answer e.g.

- Is the x co-ordinate positive?
- Is the y co-ordinate greater than 4?

After his/her turn a player may say 'I think the point is...' If the point is correct the player wins, if not he takes no further part in this round of the game.

Clearly the above are efficient questions. Players will need to experiment with questions until they stop asking questions such as: Is it (2,4)? The teacher may choose to call attention to the inefficiency or efficiency of a particular question, but should not suggest forms of question.

Loop Games

Introduction

This form of Loop game was invented by Adrian Pinel. He has developed many of these games for use at primary level. He wrote about them in MT 184. They differ from the style of game often called 'Follow Me' in that they are made up of a number of sub-loops which interlock thus allowing the cards to be played in many different orders. Each sub-loop is itself a complete, but unique loop.

The loop games included here vary considerably in type and purpose. The two add and subtract x games each work on collecting terms. They also develop the skill of operating on an expression by, for example, adding 3x to it. These games have been used successfully in top primary classes. The function loop games were developed to help pupils learn to read complex algebraic expressions. Even the harder of these two games was played successfully by year 8 during the research which was the basis of these games. The mathematical symbolism seemed to give purpose and meaning to the game and it was mastered rapidly. These games also contain the idea of a function as the value is substituted into the function on the card. The two quadratic games were developed to show that games could also have a role in the work of older and more able pupils.

The sets of cards given here will allow for up to 5 players. However, the games work particularly well if the players are 3 pairs of pupils as this allows discussion.

When the pupils first meet a new set of loop cards, two devices can help them to get sufficiently fluent with the cards to make the game 'flow'. Firstly, a set of 6 or 12 display size cards can be prepared and given to individual pupils. They then come out in turn and stand at the front to show the loop. Secondly, when a group is given the cards to play with, members of the group can be asked to check that all the cards are there by separating out the loops and making sure each fits together correctly. (This is particularly useful should you devise any new loop cards of your own!). Either or both devices can be used depending on the difficulty of the game.

The cards should not be set out in a long line as in dominoes as this causes problems in the classroom situation. I have found that the best method is to pile up the cards as they are played, but for the new card played to be put alongside the pile for the next player to check and put on top of the pile.

The instructions suggest that the cards are placed face upwards on the table. This has two advantages, it allows for a measure of peer tuition and for an element of strategy which is much enjoyed by the pupils.

Loop Games Rules 1

Games for 3 to 5 players

Deal the pack equally to each player

Each card has a 'value' in the top left hand corner.

Each card has an 'operation' which is carried out on the value to determine the value of the card which must be played next.

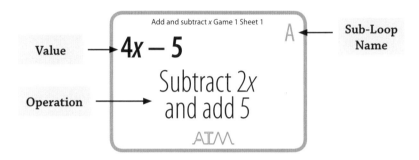

Players put their cards face up on the table in front of them.

One player chooses any card to start the game.

Players then, in turn play a card with the correct next value. See overleaf for more details about calculating this value.

A player who is unable to play 'knocks' and the play moves to the next player. The first player to get rid of all of his/her cards is the winner.

If no-one can play, then the last person who played a card plays any card to restart the game.

Instructions for specific loop games

Add and subtract *x* games, Loopy powers and Quadratic loops

Carry out the instruction given in the centre of the card to find the next card.

Function Loops 1 and 2

The expression in the centre should be regarded as a function and the value of the card sustituted in to find the next value e.g.

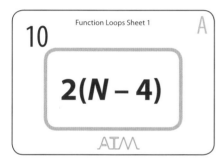

What went in

In this game it is important that the pupils understand that the new card is played to the left of the previous one, thus supplying the number that was needed as the input to that machine to produce the given output.

So the correct card to play after e.g.

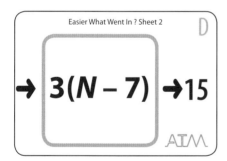 is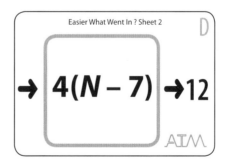

since they fit

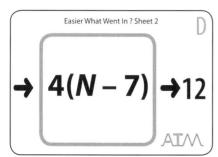 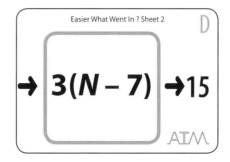

Add and Subtract x. Game 1 — Sheet 1

Add and subtract x Game 1 Sheet 1

A

$4x - 5$

Subtract $2x$
and add 5

AIM

A

$2x$

Add x

AIM

A

$3x$

Subtract x
and add 2

AIM

A

$2x + 2$

Subtract 5

AIM

A

$2x - 3$

Add x and
add 6

AIM

A

$3x + 3$

Add x and
subtract 8

AIM

B

$5x + 1$

Subtract $3x$
and subtract 4

AIM

B

$2x - 3$

Add $3x$

AIM

B

$5x - 3$

Subtract $2x$
and add 2

AIM

B

$3x - 1$

Add x and
subtract 4

AIM

B

$4x - 5$

Subtract $2x$
and add 5

AIM

B

$2x$

Add $3x$
and add 1

AIM

C

$4x - 5$

Subtract $2x$
and add 2

AIM

C

$2x - 3$

Add $4x$ and
add 4

AIM

C

$6x + 1$

Subtract $4x$
and subtract 1

AIM

C

$2x$

Add $3x$ and
subtract 3

AIM

C

$5x - 3$

Subtract $2x$
and add 6

AIM

C

$3x + 3$

Add x and
subtract 8

AIM

26

Add and subtract *x* Game 1 Sheet 2 D **$5x + 1$** Subtract 3*x* and subtract 1 ATM	Add and subtract *x* Game 1 Sheet 2 D **$2x$** Add 3*x* and subtract 1 ATM	Add and subtract *x* Game 1 Sheet 2 D **$5x - 1$** Subtract 2*x* and add 4 ATM
Add and subtract *x* Game 1 Sheet 2 D **$3x + 3$** Subtract *x* and subtract 1 ATM	Add and subtract *x* Game 1 Sheet 2 D **$2x + 2$** Add 4*x* and subtract 1 ATM	Add and subtract *x* Game 1 Sheet 2 D **$6x + 1$** Subtract *x* ATM
Add and subtract *x* Game 1 Sheet 2 E **$6x + 1$** Subtract 3*x* and subtract 2 ATM	Add and subtract *x* Game 1 Sheet 2 E **$3x - 1$** Add 4 ATM	Add and subtract *x* Game 1 Sheet 2 E **$3x + 3$** Subtract *x* and subtract 3 ATM
Add and subtract *x* Game 1 Sheet 2 E **$2x$** Add 2 ATM	Add and subtract *x* Game 1 Sheet 2 E **$2x + 2$** Add 3*x* and subtract 5 ATM	Add and subtract *x* Game 1 Sheet 2 E **$5x - 3$** Add *x* and add 4 ATM
Add and subtract *x* Game 1 Sheet 2 F **$4x - 5$** Add *x* and add 6 ATM	Add and subtract *x* Game 1 Sheet 2 F **$5x + 1$** Subtract 2 ATM	Add and subtract *x* Game 1 Sheet 2 F **$5x - 1$** Subtract 3*x* and add 1 ATM
Add and subtract *x* Game 1 Sheet 2 F **$2x$** Add *x* and subtract 1 ATM	Add and subtract *x* Game 1 Sheet 2 F **$3x - 1$** Add 1 ATM	Add and subtract *x* Game 1 Sheet 2 F **$3x$** Add *x* and subtract 5 ATM

Add and Subtract x. Game 2 — Sheet 1

A

$3 + 2x$

Subtract $3x$
and subtract 1

ATM

A

$2 - x$

Subtract x
and add 3

ATM

A

$5 - 2x$

Subtract 1
and add $3x$

ATM

A

$4 + x$

Subtract 3

ATM

A

$1 + x$

Add 5 and
subtract $4x$

ATM

A

$6 - 3x$

Subtract 3
and add $5x$

ATM

B

$3 - 2x$

Add 2

ATM

B

$5 - 2x$

Add $5x$

ATM

B

$5 + 3x$

Add x
and add 1

ATM

B

$6 + 4x$

Subtract $3x$
and subtract 5

ATM

B

$1 + x$

Add x
and add 2

ATM

B

$3 + 2x$

Subtract $4x$

ATM

C

$3 + 2x$

Subtract $4x$
and add 2

ATM

C

$5 - 2x$

Add $3x$
and subtract 4

ATM

C

$1 + x$

Add $3x$
and add 5

ATM

C

$6 + 4x$

Subtract $3x$
and subtract 2

ATM

C

$4 + x$

Subtract 1
and add $2x$

ATM

C

$3 + 3x$

Subtract x

ATM

Add and Subtract *x*. Game 2 — Sheet 2

Add and subtract x Game 2 Sheet 2
3 + 2*x*

Subtract 4*x*

ATM

D

Add and subtract x Game 2 Sheet 2
3 − 2*x*

Subtract 2
and add *x*

ATM

D

Add and subtract x Game 2 Sheet 2
1 − *x*

Add 1

ATM

D

Add and subtract x Game 2 Sheet 2
2 − *x*

Add 2*x* and
subtract 1

ATM

D

Add and subtract x Game 2 Sheet 2
1 + *x*

Add 2*x* and
add 4

ATM

D

Add and subtract x Game 2 Sheet 2
5 + 3*x*

Subtract *x* and
subtract 2

ATM

D

Add and subtract x Game 2 Sheet 2
3 + 3*x*

Subtract 2*x*
and add 1

ATM

E

Add and subtract x Game 2 Sheet 2
4 + *x*

Add 3*x*
and add 2

ATM

E

Add and subtract x Game 2 Sheet 2
6 + 4*x*

Subtract 3*x*
and subtract 5

ATM

E

Add and subtract x Game 2 Sheet 2
1 + *x*

Subtract 4*x*
and add 5

ATM

E

Add and subtract x Game 2 Sheet 2
6 − 3*x*

Add 6*x* and
subtract 1

ATM

E

Add and subtract x Game 2 Sheet 2
5 + 3*x*

Subtract 2

ATM

E

Add and subtract x Game 2 Sheet 2
3 − 2*x*

Add 5*x*

ATM

F

Add and subtract x Game 2 Sheet 2
3 + 3*x*

Subtract 2*x*
and subtract 2

ATM

F

Add and subtract x Game 2 Sheet 2
1 + *x*

Add 3

ATM

F

Add and subtract x Game 2 Sheet 2
4 + *x*

Subtract 4*x*
and add 2

ATM

F

Add and subtract x Game 2 Sheet 2
6 − 3*x*

Add 2*x* and
subtract 5

ATM

F

Add and subtract x Game 2 Sheet 2
1 − *x*

Subtract *x*
and add 2

ATM

F

Function Loops

18 Function Loops Sheet 1 A $$\dfrac{N}{2} + 1$$ AIM	**10** Function Loops Sheet 1 A $$2(N-4)$$ AIM	**12** Function Loops Sheet 1 A $$N + 3$$ AIM
15 Function Loops Sheet 1 A $$\dfrac{N-10}{5}$$ AIM	**1** Function Loops Sheet 1 A $$4N + 1$$ AIM	**5** Function Loops Sheet 1 A $$3N + 3$$ AIM
12 Function Loops Sheet 1 B $$2(N-3)$$ AIM	**18** Function Loops Sheet 1 B $$\dfrac{N-8}{2}$$ AIM	**5** Function Loops Sheet 1 B $$2N - 8$$ AIM
2 Function Loops Sheet 1 B $$5N - 2$$ AIM	**8** Function Loops Sheet 1 B $$N + 7$$ AIM	**15** Function Loops Sheet 1 B $$N - 3$$ AIM
12 Function Loops Sheet 1 C $$2N - 10$$ AIM	**14** Function Loops Sheet 1 C $$N - 7$$ AIM	**7** Function Loops Sheet 1 C $$2N - 4$$ AIM
10 Function Loops Sheet 1 C $$\dfrac{N}{2} + 10$$ AIM	**15** Function Loops Sheet 1 C $$N + 5$$ AIM	**20** Function Loops Sheet 1 C $$\dfrac{N}{2} + 2$$ AIM

Function Loops

8 — Function Loops Sheet 2 — D $2(N-1)$ ATM	**14** — Function Loops Sheet 2 — D $N+6$ ATM	**20** — Function Loops Sheet 2 — D $\dfrac{N}{10}$ ATM
2 — Function Loops Sheet 2 — D $5N+2$ ATM	**12** — Function Loops Sheet 2 — A $2N-6$ ATM	**18** — Function Loops Sheet 2 — D $N-10$ ATM
8 — Function Loops Sheet 2 — E $2N+2$ ATM	**18** — Function Loops Sheet 2 — E $N-6$ ATM	**12** — Function Loops Sheet 2 — E $\dfrac{N}{2}-5$ ATM
1 — Function Loops Sheet 2 — E $8N-1$ ATM	**7** — Function Loops Sheet 2 — E $2N+6$ ATM	**20** — Function Loops Sheet 2 — E $\dfrac{N}{2}-2$ ATM
12 — Function Loops Sheet 2 — F $N+8$ ATM	**20** — Function Loops Sheet 2 — F $\dfrac{N}{2}+4$ ATM	**14** — Function Loops Sheet 2 — F $\dfrac{N}{7}$ ATM
2 — Function Loops Sheet 2 — F $5N-3$ ATM	**7** — Function Loops Sheet 2 — F $N-2$ ATM	**5** — Function Loops Sheet 2 — F $2N+2$ ATM

Harder Function Loops

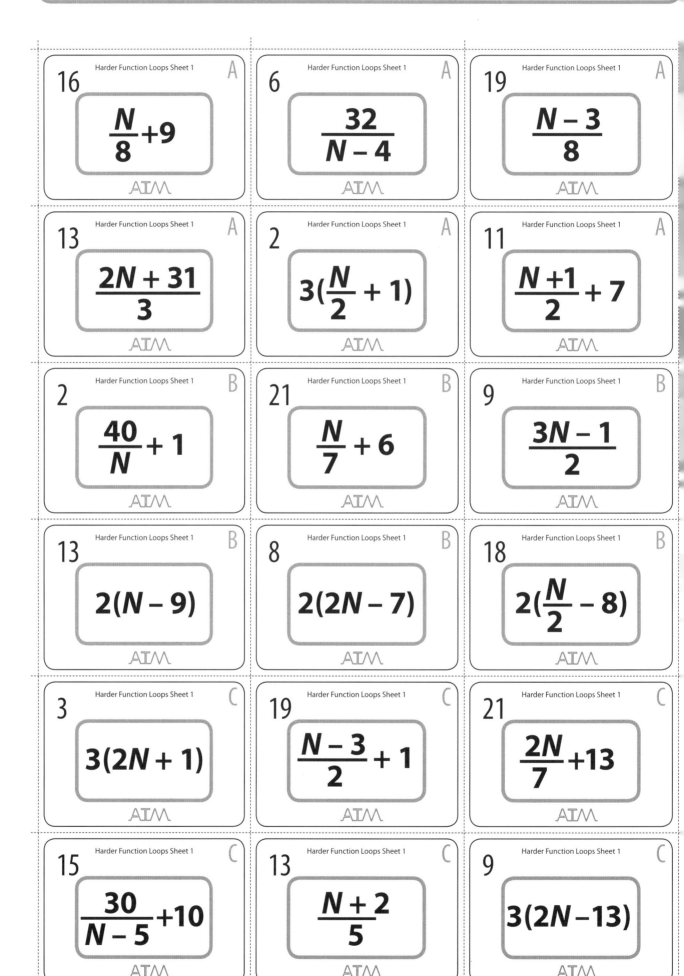

16 — Harder Function Loops Sheet 1 — A

$$\frac{N}{8}+9$$

AIM

6 — Harder Function Loops Sheet 1 — A

$$\frac{32}{N-4}$$

AIM

19 — Harder Function Loops Sheet 1 — A

$$\frac{N-3}{8}$$

AIM

13 — Harder Function Loops Sheet 1 — A

$$\frac{2N+31}{3}$$

AIM

2 — Harder Function Loops Sheet 1 — A

$$3\left(\frac{N}{2}+1\right)$$

AIM

11 — Harder Function Loops Sheet 1 — A

$$\frac{N+1}{2}+7$$

AIM

2 — Harder Function Loops Sheet 1 — B

$$\frac{40}{N}+1$$

AIM

21 — Harder Function Loops Sheet 1 — B

$$\frac{N}{7}+6$$

AIM

9 — Harder Function Loops Sheet 1 — B

$$\frac{3N-1}{2}$$

AIM

13 — Harder Function Loops Sheet 1 — B

$$2(N-9)$$

AIM

8 — Harder Function Loops Sheet 1 — B

$$2(2N-7)$$

AIM

18 — Harder Function Loops Sheet 1 — B

$$2\left(\frac{N}{2}-8\right)$$

AIM

3 — Harder Function Loops Sheet 1 — C

$$3(2N+1)$$

AIM

19 — Harder Function Loops Sheet 1 — C

$$\frac{N-3}{2}+1$$

AIM

21 — Harder Function Loops Sheet 1 — C

$$\frac{2N}{7}+13$$

AIM

15 — Harder Function Loops Sheet 1 — C

$$\frac{30}{N-5}+10$$

AIM

13 — Harder Function Loops Sheet 1 — C

$$\frac{N+2}{5}$$

AIM

9 — Harder Function Loops Sheet 1 — C

$$3(2N-13)$$

AIM

Harder Function Loops

Sheet 2

11 — D

$$8(13 - N)$$

ATM

8 — D

$$3(N - 1)$$

ATM

21 — D

$$\frac{N + 12}{3}$$

ATM

15 — D

$$2(19 - N)$$

ATM

13 — D

$$3(N - 8)$$

ATM

16 — D

$$\frac{N + 4}{2} + 3$$

ATM

8 — E

$$7(11 - N)$$

ATM

21 — E

$$\frac{N + 7}{7} - 1$$

ATM

3 — E

$$3(8 - N)$$

ATM

15 — E

$$\frac{30}{N} + 4$$

ATM

6 — E

$$\frac{18}{N} + 10$$

ATM

13 — E

$$\frac{2N - 2}{3}$$

ATM

13 — F

$$\frac{3N - 1}{2}$$

ATM

9 — F

$$\frac{32}{N - 7}$$

ATM

16 — F

$$\frac{N + 10}{2}$$

ATM

19 — F

$$\frac{N - 1}{3}$$

ATM

6 — F

$$\frac{24}{2N - 4}$$

ATM

3 — F

$$\frac{45}{2N - 1}$$

ATM

Loopy Powers 1

Loopy Powers 1 Sheet 1 A a^2 $\times\, a$ AIM	Loopy Powers 1 Sheet 1 A a^3 $\times\, 2$ AIM	Loopy Powers 1 Sheet 1 A $2a^3$ $\times\, 3$ AIM
Loopy Powers 1 Sheet 1 A $6a^3$ $\div\, 3$ AIM	Loopy Powers 1 Sheet 1 A $3a^3$ $\div\, 2a^3$ AIM	Loopy Powers 1 Sheet 1 A a $\times\, a$ AIM
Loopy Powers 1 Sheet 1 B a^4 $\times\, 2$ AIM	Loopy Powers 1 Sheet 1 B $2a^4$ $\div\, a^2$ AIM	Loopy Powers 1 Sheet 1 B $2a^2$ $\div\, a$ AIM
Loopy Powers 1 Sheet 1 B $2a$ $\div\, 2$ AIM	Loopy Powers 1 Sheet 1 B a $\times\, 6a^2$ AIM	Loopy Powers 1 Sheet 1 B $6a^3$ $\div\, 6$ and $\times\, a$ AIM
Loopy Powers 1 Sheet 1 C a^4 $\div\, a$ AIM	Loopy Powers 1 Sheet 1 C a^3 $\times\, 3$ AIM	Loopy Powers 1 Sheet 1 C $3a^3$ $\times\, 2$ AIM
Loopy Powers 1 Sheet 1 C $6a^3$ $\div\, a^2$ AIM	Loopy Powers 1 Sheet 1 C $6a$ $\div\, 3$ AIM	Loopy Powers 1 Sheet 1 C $2a$ $\div\, 2$ and $\times\, a^3$ AIM

Loopy Powers 1

Loopy Powers 1 Sheet 2 — D $6a^3$ $\div\ 3$ and $\times\ a$ ATM	Loopy Powers 1 Sheet 2 — D $2a^4$ $\div\ a^3$ ATM	Loopy Powers 1 Sheet 2 — D $2a$ $\times\ a^4$ ATM
Loopy Powers 1 Sheet 2 — D $2a^5$ $\div\ a^2$ ATM	Loopy Powers 1 Sheet 2 — D $2a^3$ $\div\ 2$ and $\times\ a$ ATM	Loopy Powers 1 Sheet 2 — D a^4 $\div\ a$ and $\times\ 6$ ATM
Loopy Powers 1 Sheet 2 — E a^3 $\times\ 2a$ ATM	Loopy Powers 1 Sheet 2 — E $2a^4$ $\times\ 3$ and $\div\ 2a$ ATM	Loopy Powers 1 Sheet 2 — E $3a^3$ $\times\ a$ and $\div\ 3$ ATM
Loopy Powers 1 Sheet 2 — E a^4 $\times\ 2$ and $\div\ a^2$ ATM	Loopy Powers 1 Sheet 2 — E $2a^2$ $\times\ 3a$ ATM	Loopy Powers 1 Sheet 2 — E $6a^3$ $\div\ 6$ ATM
Loopy Powers 1 Sheet 2 — F a $\times\ 3a^2$ ATM	Loopy Powers 1 Sheet 2 — F $3a^3$ $\times\ 2a^2$ and $\div\ 3$ ATM	Loopy Powers 1 Sheet 2 — F $2a^5$ $\times\ 3$ and $\div\ a^2$ ATM
Loopy Powers 1 Sheet 2 — F $6a^3$ $\div\ 3$ ATM	Loopy Powers 1 Sheet 2 — F $2a^3$ $\times\ 3$ and $\div\ a^2$ ATM	Loopy Powers 1 Sheet 2 — F $6a$ $\div\ 6$ ATM

Loopy Powers 2

ca Divide by *c* A AIM	*a* Multiply by *b* A AIM	*ab* Divide by *a* A AIM
b Multiply by *bc* A AIM	b^2c Divide by b^2 A AIM	*c* Multiply by *a* A AIM
b^2 Multiply by c^2 B AIM	b^2c^2 Divide by b^2c and multiply by *a* B AIM	*ca* Divide by *a* and multiply by *c* B AIM
c^2 Divide by *c* B AIM	*c* Divide by *c* and multiply by *b* B AIM	*b* Multiply by *b* B AIM
b^2 Multiply by *c* C AIM	b^2c Divide by *b* C AIM	*cb* Divide by *c* C AIM
b Divide by *b* and multiply by c^2 C AIM	c^2 Divide by c^2 and multiply by *a* C AIM	*a* Divide by *a* and multiply by b^2 C AIM

Loopy Powers 2 Sheet 1

Loopy Powers 2

Loopy Powers 2 Sheet 2 D c^2 Multiply by b^2 ATM	Loopy Powers 2 Sheet 2 D b^2c^2 Divide by bc^2 ATM	Loopy Powers 2 Sheet 2 D b Multiply by ba ATM
Loopy Powers 2 Sheet 2 D b^2a Divide by b ATM	Loopy Powers 2 Sheet 2 D ab Multiply by b and divide by a ATM	Loopy Powers 2 Sheet 2 D b^2 Divide by b^2 and multiply by c^2 ATM
Loopy Powers 2 Sheet 2 E b Multiply by b ATM	Loopy Powers 2 Sheet 2 E b^2 Multiply by c^2 ATM	Loopy Powers 2 Sheet 2 E b^2c^2 Divide by c ATM
Loopy Powers 2 Sheet 2 E b^2c Divide by b^2 and multiply by a ATM	Loopy Powers 2 Sheet 2 E ca Divide by c ATM	Loopy Powers 2 Sheet 2 E a Divide by a and multiply by b ATM
Loopy Powers 2 Sheet 2 F c Multiply by b^2 ATM	Loopy Powers 2 Sheet 2 F b^2c Divide by c and multiply by a ATM	Loopy Powers 2 Sheet 2 F b^2a Divide by b ATM
Loopy Powers 2 Sheet 2 F ab Divide by a ATM	Loopy Powers 2 Sheet 2 F b Multiply by c ATM	Loopy Powers 2 Sheet 2 F cb Divide by b ATM

Quadratic Add and Subtract

Sheet 1

Quadratic add and subtract Sheet 1 A

$x^2 - 3x + 2$

Add $4x$
and subtract 3

AIM

Quadratic add and subtract Sheet 1 A

$x^2 + x - 1$

Subtract $(2x^2 + x)$
and add 4

AIM

Quadratic add and subtract Sheet 1 A

$3 - x^2$

Add $3x^2$ and
subtract 1

AIM

Quadratic add and subtract Sheet 1 A

$2x^2 + 2$

Add x^2 and
subtract $(3x + 2)$

AIM

Quadratic add and subtract Sheet 1 A

$3x^2 - 3x$

Add $3x + 4$

AIM

Quadratic add and subtract Sheet 1 A

$3x^2 + 4$

Subtract
$(2x^2 + 3x + 2)$

AIM

Quadratic add and subtract Sheet 1 B

$4 - 2x^2$

Subtract 3
and add $x^2 + x$

AIM

Quadratic add and subtract Sheet 1 B

$1 + x - x^2$

Add $4x^2$
and subtract 6

AIM

Quadratic add and subtract Sheet 1 B

$3x^2 + x - 5$

Subtract $4x$
and add 5

AIM

Quadratic add and subtract Sheet 1 B

$3x^2 - 3x$

Add 2 and
subtract $2x^2$

AIM

Quadratic add and subtract Sheet 1 B

$x^2 - 3x + 2$

Subtract 3
and add $4x$

AIM

Quadratic add and subtract Sheet 1 B

$x^2 + x - 1$

Add 5
subtract $(3x^2 + x)$

AIM

Quadratic add and subtract Sheet 1 C

$x^2 - 3x + 2$

Subtract $(2x^2 + 1)$
and add $4x$

AIM

Quadratic add and subtract Sheet 1 C

$1 + x - x^2$

Add $6x$ and
subtract $(x^2 + 1)$

AIM

Quadratic add and subtract Sheet 1 C

$7x - 2x^2$

Subtract $(6x + 1)$
and add $3x^2$

AIM

Quadratic add and subtract Sheet 1 C

$x^2 + x - 1$

Add $2x^2$ and
subtract 4

AIM

Quadratic add and subtract Sheet 1 C

$3x^2 + x - 5$

Subtract x
and add 9

AIM

Quadratic add and subtract Sheet 1 C

$3x^2 + 4$

Subtract
$(2x^2 + 3x + 2)$

AIM

Quadratic Add and Subtract

Sheet 2

Quadratic add and subtract Sheet 2
D

$4 - 2x^2$

Add $3x^2 + x$
and subtract 5

AIM

Quadratic add and subtract Sheet 2
D

$x^2 + x - 1$

Add $x^2 + 1$
and subtract x

AIM

Quadratic add and subtract Sheet 2
D

$2x^2$

Add $x^2 + 4$

AIM

Quadratic add and subtract Sheet 2
D

$3x^2 + 4$

Subtract $(x^2 + 2)$

AIM

Quadratic add and subtract Sheet 2
D

$2x^2 + 2$

Subtract $(4x^2 + 2)$
and add $7x$

AIM

Quadratic add and subtract Sheet 2
D

$7x - 2x^2$

Subtract $7x$
and add 4

AIM

Quadratic add and subtract Sheet 2
E

$7x - 2x^2$

Subtract $10x$
and add $5x^2$

AIM

Quadratic add and subtract Sheet 2
E

$3x^2 - 3x$

Add $3x + 4$

AIM

Quadratic add and subtract Sheet 2
E

$3x^2 + 4$

Subtract $(2x^2 + 5)$
and add x

AIM

Quadratic add and subtract Sheet 2
E

$x^2 + x - 1$

Add $x^2 + 3$
and subtract x

AIM

Quadratic add and subtract Sheet 2
E

$2x^2 + 2$

Add $x^2 + x$
and subtract 7

AIM

Quadratic add and subtract Sheet 2
E

$3x^2 + x - 5$

Subtract $5x^2$
and add $6x + 5$

AIM

Quadratic add and subtract Sheet 2
F

$x^2 - 3x + 2$

Add $3x + 2$
and subtract $3x^2$

AIM

Quadratic add and subtract Sheet 2
F

$4 - 2x^2$

Add $4x^2$ and
subtract 4

AIM

Quadratic add and subtract Sheet 2
F

$2x^2$

Subtract $(x^2 + 1)$
and add x

AIM

Quadratic add and subtract Sheet 2
F

$x^2 + x - 1$

Add $2x^2 + 1$
and subtract $4x$

AIM

Quadratic add and subtract Sheet 2
F

$3x^2 - 3x$

Add $3x + 3$
and subtract $4x^2$

AIM

Quadratic add and subtract Sheet 2
F

$3 - x^2$

Add $2x^2$ and
subtract $(3x + 1)$

AIM

Easier What Went In?

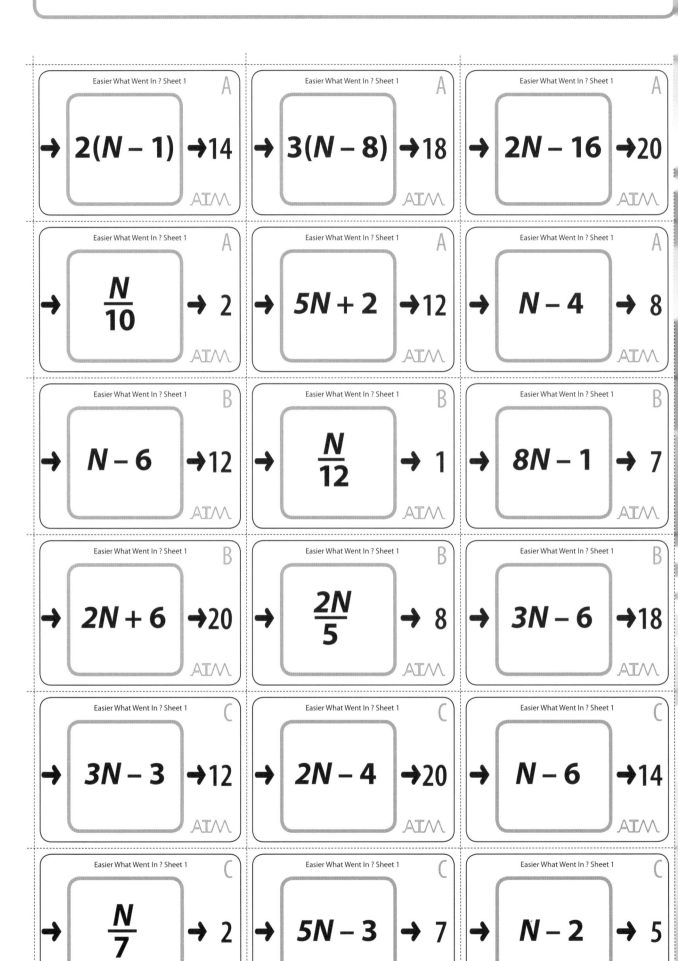

Easier What Went In ? Sheet 1 — A

→ $2(N - 1)$ →14

Easier What Went In ? Sheet 1 — A

→ $3(N - 8)$ →18

Easier What Went In ? Sheet 1 — A

→ $2N - 16$ →20

Easier What Went In ? Sheet 1 — A

→ $\dfrac{N}{10}$ → 2

Easier What Went In ? Sheet 1 — A

→ $5N + 2$ →12

Easier What Went In ? Sheet 1 — A

→ $N - 4$ → 8

Easier What Went In ? Sheet 1 — B

→ $N - 6$ →12

Easier What Went In ? Sheet 1 — B

→ $\dfrac{N}{12}$ → 1

Easier What Went In ? Sheet 1 — B

→ $8N - 1$ → 7

Easier What Went In ? Sheet 1 — B

→ $2N + 6$ →20

Easier What Went In ? Sheet 1 — B

→ $\dfrac{2N}{5}$ → 8

Easier What Went In ? Sheet 1 — B

→ $3N - 6$ →18

Easier What Went In ? Sheet 1 — C

→ $3N - 3$ →12

Easier What Went In ? Sheet 1 — C

→ $2N - 4$ →20

Easier What Went In ? Sheet 1 — C

→ $N - 6$ →14

Easier What Went In ? Sheet 1 — C

→ $\dfrac{N}{7}$ → 2

Easier What Went In ? Sheet 1 — C

→ $5N - 3$ → 7

Easier What Went In ? Sheet 1 — C

→ $N - 2$ → 5

Easier What Went In?

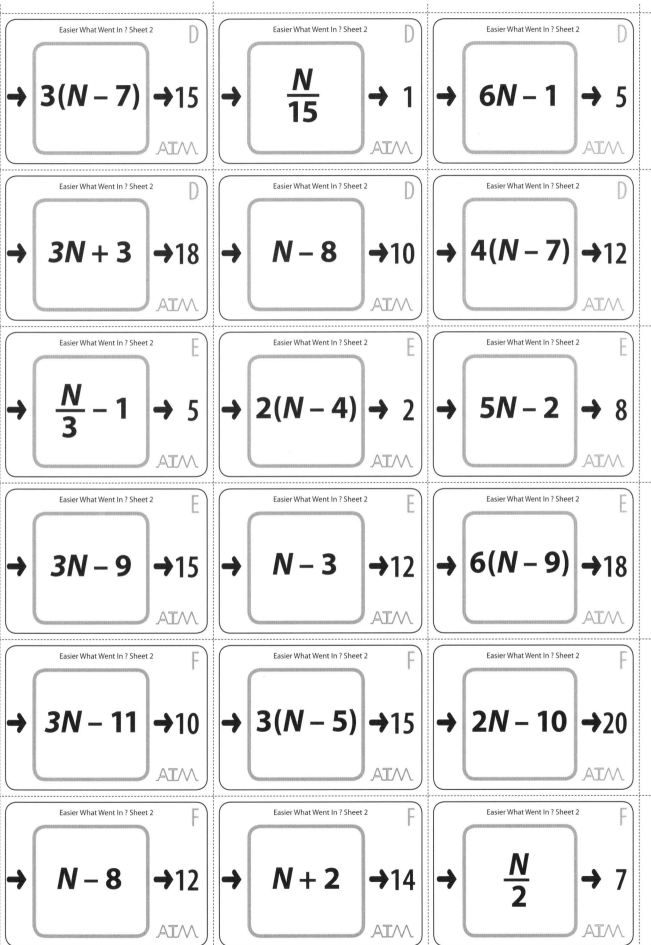

Easier What Went In ? Sheet 2 — D

→ $3(N - 7)$ →15

Easier What Went In ? Sheet 2 — D

→ $\dfrac{N}{15}$ → 1

Easier What Went In ? Sheet 2 — D

→ $6N - 1$ → 5

Easier What Went In ? Sheet 2 — D

→ $3N + 3$ →18

Easier What Went In ? Sheet 2 — D

→ $N - 8$ →10

Easier What Went In ? Sheet 2 — D

→ $4(N - 7)$ →12

Easier What Went In ? Sheet 2 — E

→ $\dfrac{N}{3} - 1$ → 5

Easier What Went In ? Sheet 2 — E

→ $2(N - 4)$ → 2

Easier What Went In ? Sheet 2 — E

→ $5N - 2$ → 8

Easier What Went In ? Sheet 2 — E

→ $3N - 9$ →15

Easier What Went In ? Sheet 2 — E

→ $N - 3$ →12

Easier What Went In ? Sheet 2 — E

→ $6(N - 9)$ →18

Easier What Went In ? Sheet 2 — F

→ $3N - 11$ →10

Easier What Went In ? Sheet 2 — F

→ $3(N - 5)$ →15

Easier What Went In ? Sheet 2 — F

→ $2N - 10$ →20

Easier What Went In ? Sheet 2 — F

→ $N - 8$ →12

Easier What Went In ? Sheet 2 — F

→ $N + 2$ →14

Easier What Went In ? Sheet 2 — F

→ $\dfrac{N}{2}$ → 7

ATM

What Went In?

Row 1

A — What Went In ? Sheet 1

$\rightarrow$ $3(N-7)$ $\rightarrow 15$ ATM

A — What Went In ? Sheet 1

$\rightarrow$ $\dfrac{N-10}{5}$ $\rightarrow 1$ ATM

A — What Went In ? Sheet 1

$\rightarrow$ $8N-3$ $\rightarrow 5$ ATM

Row 2

A — What Went In ? Sheet 1

$\rightarrow$ $3(N+1)$ $\rightarrow 18$ ATM

A — What Went In ? Sheet 1

$\rightarrow$ $\dfrac{N}{2}+1$ $\rightarrow 10$ ATM

A — What Went In ? Sheet 1

$\rightarrow$ $2(N-4)$ $\rightarrow 12$ ATM

Row 3

B — What Went In ? Sheet 1

$\rightarrow$ $\dfrac{N-8}{2}$ $\rightarrow 5$ ATM

B — What Went In ? Sheet 1

$\rightarrow$ $2N-8$ $\rightarrow 2$ ATM

B — What Went In ? Sheet 1

$\rightarrow$ $5N-2$ $\rightarrow 8$ ATM

Row 4

B — What Went In ? Sheet 1

$\rightarrow$ $3(N-3)$ $\rightarrow 15$ ATM

B — What Went In ? Sheet 1

$\rightarrow$ $\dfrac{N}{3}+7$ $\rightarrow 12$ ATM

B — What Went In ? Sheet 1

$\rightarrow$ $2(N-3)$ $\rightarrow 18$ ATM

Row 5

C — What Went In ? Sheet 1

$\rightarrow$ $2N-4$ $\rightarrow 10$ ATM

C — What Went In ? Sheet 1

$\rightarrow$ $\dfrac{N+20}{2}$ $\rightarrow 15$ ATM

C — What Went In ? Sheet 1

$\rightarrow$ $N+5$ $\rightarrow 20$ ATM

Row 6

C — What Went In ? Sheet 1

$\rightarrow$ $\dfrac{N}{2}+2$ $\rightarrow 12$ ATM

C — What Went In ? Sheet 1

$\rightarrow$ $2N-10$ $\rightarrow 14$ ATM

C — What Went In ? Sheet 1

$\rightarrow$ $N-7$ $\rightarrow 7$ ATM

What Went In?

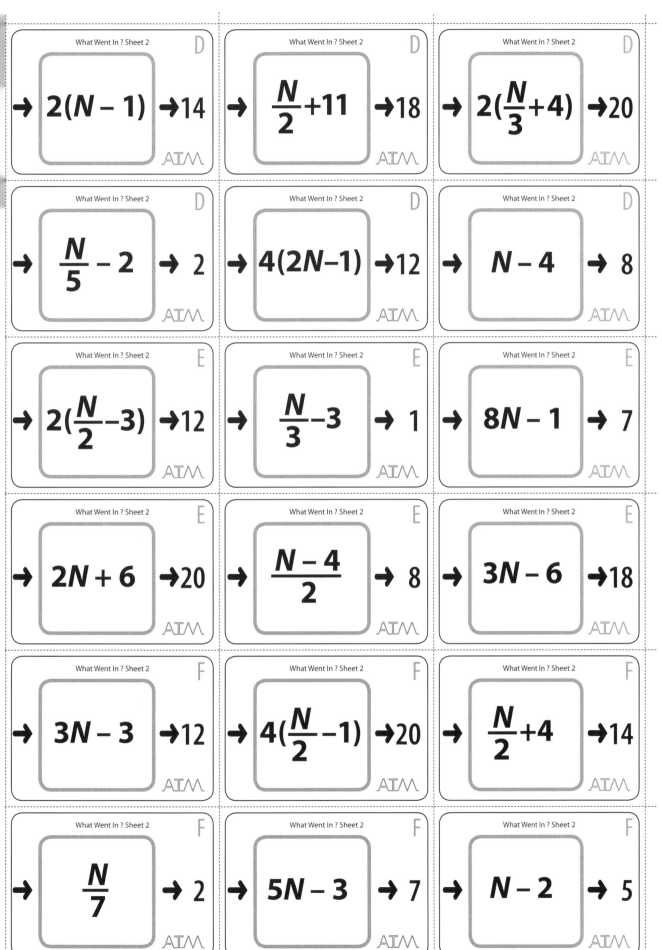

→ $2(N-1)$ →14   D

→ $\dfrac{N}{2}+11$ →18   D

→ $2\left(\dfrac{N}{3}+4\right)$ →20   D

→ $\dfrac{N}{5}-2$ → 2   D

→ $4(2N-1)$ →12   D

→ $N-4$ → 8   D

→ $2\left(\dfrac{N}{2}-3\right)$ →12   E

→ $\dfrac{N}{3}-3$ → 1   E

→ $8N-1$ → 7   E

→ $2N+6$ →20   E

→ $\dfrac{N-4}{2}$ → 8   E

→ $3N-6$ →18   E

→ $3N-3$ →12   F

→ $4\left(\dfrac{N}{2}-1\right)$ →20   F

→ $\dfrac{N}{2}+4$ →14   F

→ $\dfrac{N}{7}$ → 2   F

→ $5N-3$ → 7   F

→ $N-2$ → 5   F

Each card labelled: What Went In ? Sheet 2 — ATM

Quadratic Loop Game A

Quadratic Loop Game A Sheet 1 — A $x^2 + 3x + 2$ Factorise AIM	Quadratic Loop Game A Sheet 1 — A $x + 4$ $\times (x - 2)$ AIM	Quadratic Loop Game A Sheet 1 — A $(x + 2)(x + 1)$ Divide by $(x + 1)$ AIM
Quadratic Loop Game A Sheet 1 — A $x^2 + 3x - 4$ Factorise AIM	Quadratic Loop Game A Sheet 1 — A $x + 2$ $\times (x - 1)$ AIM	Quadratic Loop Game A Sheet 1 — A $x^2 + 2x - 8$ Add $x + 10$ AIM
Quadratic Loop Game A Sheet 1 — A $(x + 4)(x - 1)$ Divide by $x - 1$ AIM	Quadratic Loop Game A Sheet 1 — A $x^2 + x - 2$ Add $2x - 2$ AIM	Quadratic Loop Game A Sheet 1 — B $(x - 3)(x - 4)$ Divide by $(x - 3)$ AIM
Quadratic Loop Game A Sheet 1 — B $x - 5$ $\times (x - 2)$ AIM	Quadratic Loop Game A Sheet 1 — B $x^2 - 4x$ Subtract 5 AIM	Quadratic Loop Game A Sheet 1 — B $x^2 - 7x + 10$ Add 2 AIM
Quadratic Loop Game A Sheet 1 — B $x^2 - 4x - 5$ Factorise AIM	Quadratic Loop Game A Sheet 1 — B $x^2 - 7x + 12$ Factorise AIM	Quadratic Loop Game A Sheet 1 — B $(x - 5)(x + 1)$ Divide by $(x + 1)$ AIM
Quadratic Loop Game A Sheet 1 — B $x - 4$ Multiply by x AIM	Quadratic Loop Game A Sheet 1 — C $x^2 - 2x - 8$ Subtract $5x - 20$ AIM	Quadratic Loop Game A Sheet 1 — C $x - 3$ Multiply by x AIM

Quadratic Loop Game A

Quadratic Loop Game A Sheet 2 C $x - 4$ Multiply by $x + 2$ ATM	**Quadratic Loop Game A Sheet 2** C $x^2 - 3x$ Subtract $2x - 4$ ATM	**Quadratic Loop Game A Sheet 2** C $x^2 - 7x + 12$ Factorise ATM
Quadratic Loop Game A Sheet 2 C $(x - 3)(x - 4)$ Divide by $(x - 4)$ ATM	**Quadratic Loop Game A Sheet 2** C $x^2 - 5x + 4$ Factorise ATM	**Quadratic Loop Game A Sheet 2** C $(x - 1)(x - 4)$ Divide by $x - 1$ ATM
Quadratic Loop Game A Sheet 2 D $x^2 - x - 6$ Subtract $3x - 1$ ATM	**Quadratic Loop Game A Sheet 2** D $x^2 + 3x + 2$ Factorise ATM	**Quadratic Loop Game A Sheet 2** D $x^2 - 4x - 5$ Factorise ATM
Quadratic Loop Game A Sheet 2 D $(x + 1)(x + 2)$ Divide by $x + 1$ ATM	**Quadratic Loop Game A Sheet 2** D $x + 1$ Multiply by x ATM	**Quadratic Loop Game A Sheet 2** D $(x + 1)(x - 5)$ Divide by $x - 5$ ATM
Quadratic Loop Game A Sheet 2 D $x + 2$ Multiply by $(x - 3)$ ATM	**Quadratic Loop Game A Sheet 2** D $x^2 + x$ Add $2x + 2$ ATM	**Quadratic Loop Game A Sheet 2** E $x^2 - 3x - 10$ Factorise ATM
Quadratic Loop Game A Sheet 2 E $x + 2$ Multiply by $x - 1$ ATM	**Quadratic Loop Game A Sheet 2** E $(x + 2)(x - 4)$ Divide by $(x + 2)$ ATM	**Quadratic Loop Game A Sheet 2** E $x - 4$ Multiply by $(x + 3)$ ATM

Quadratic Loop Game A Sheet 3   E

$x^2 - 2x - 8$

Factorise

AIM

Quadratic Loop Game A Sheet 3   E

$x^2 + x - 2$

Subtract $3x + 6$

AIM

Quadratic Loop Game A Sheet 3   E

$(x + 2)(x - 5)$

Divide by $(x - 5)$

AIM

Quadratic Loop Game A Sheet 3   E

$x^2 - x - 12$

Subtract $2x - 2$

AIM

Quadratic Loop Game A Sheet 3   F

$x - 5$

$\times (x + 3)$

AIM

Quadratic Loop Game A Sheet 3   F

$x^2 + 2x - 35$

Factorise

AIM

Quadratic Loop Game A Sheet 3   F

$(x + 7)(x - 5)$

Divide by $x + 7$

AIM

Quadratic Loop Game A Sheet 3   F

$x^2 - 2x - 15$

Add 12

AIM

Quadratic Loop Game A Sheet 3   F

$(x - 3)(x + 1)$

Divide by $(x + 1)$

AIM

Quadratic Loop Game A Sheet 3   F

$x - 3$

$\times (x + 5)$

AIM

Quadratic Loop Game A Sheet 3   F

$x^2 + 2x - 15$

Subtract 20

AIM

Quadratic Loop Game A Sheet 3   F

$x^2 - 2x - 3$

Factorise

AIM

Quadratic Loop Game B — Sheet 1

$x^2 - 2x - 8$

Divide by $x - 4$

Multiply by $x + 5$

AIM

$x^2 + 7x + 10$

Divide by $x + 5$

Multiply by $x - 2$

AIM

$x^2 - 4$

Divide by $x + 2$

Multiply by $x - 1$

AIM

$x^2 - 3x + 2$

Divide by $x - 2$

Multiply by $x + 2$

AIM

$x^2 + x - 2$

Divide by $x + 2$

Multiply by $x - 4$

AIM

$x^2 - 5x + 4$

Divide by $x - 1$

Multiply by $x + 2$

AIM

$x^2 - 5x + 4$

Divide by $x - 4$

Multiply by $x + 3$

AIM

$x^2 + 2x - 3$

Divide by $x - 1$

Multiply by $x + 2$

AIM

$x^2 + 5x + 6$

Divide by $x + 3$

Multiply by $x + 1$

AIM

$x^2 + 3x + 2$

Divide by $x + 1$

Multiply by $x - 1$

AIM

$x^2 + x - 2$

Divide by $x - 1$

Multiply by $x - 4$

AIM

$x^2 - 2x - 8$

Divide by $x + 2$

Multiply by $x - 1$

AIM

$x^2 - 2x - 8$

Divide by $x - 4$

Multiply by $x - 2$

AIM

$x^2 - 4$

Divide by $x - 2$

Multiply by $x - 1$

AIM

$x^2 + x - 2$

Divide by $x - 1$

Multiply by $x + 5$

AIM

$x^2 + 7x + 10$

Divide by $x + 5$

Multiply by $x + 1$

AIM

$x^2 + 3x + 2$

Divide by $x + 2$

Multiply by $x - 4$

AIM

$x^2 - 3x - 4$

Divide by $x + 1$

Multiply by $x + 2$

AIM

Quadratic Loop Game B Sheet 2

D

$x^2 + 3x - 4$

Divide by $x + 4$
Multiply by $x + 3$

AIM

Quadratic Loop Game B Sheet 2

D

$x^2 + 2x - 3$

Divide by $x + 3$
Multiply by $x + 2$

AIM

Quadratic Loop Game B Sheet 2

D

$x^2 + x - 2$

Divide by $x - 1$
Multiply by $x - 4$

AIM

Quadratic Loop Game B Sheet 2

D

$x^2 - 2x - 8$

Divide by $x + 2$
Multiply by $x + 1$

AIM

Quadratic Loop Game B Sheet 2

D

$x^2 - 3x - 4$

Divide by $x - 4$
Multiply by $x - 1$

AIM

Quadratic Loop Game B Sheet 2

D

$x^2 - 1$

Divide by $x + 1$
Multiply by $x + 4$

AIM

Quadratic Loop Game B Sheet 2

E

$x^2 + 2x - 3$

Divide by $x + 3$
Multiply by $x - 4$

AIM

Quadratic Loop Game B Sheet 2

E

$x^2 - 5x + 4$

Divide by $x - 4$
Multiply by $x + 2$

AIM

Quadratic Loop Game B Sheet 2

E

$x^2 + x - 2$

Divide by $x + 2$
Multiply by $x + 1$

AIM

Quadratic Loop Game B Sheet 2

E

$x^2 - 1$

Divide by $x - 1$
Multiply by $x + 2$

AIM

Quadratic Loop Game B Sheet 2

E

$x^2 + 3x + 2$

Divide by $x + 1$
Multiply by $x + 3$

AIM

Quadratic Loop Game B Sheet 2

E

$x^2 + 5x + 6$

Divide by $x + 2$
Multiply by $x - 1$

AIM

Quadratic Loop Game B Sheet 2

F

$x^2 - 2x - 8$

Divide by $x - 4$
Multiply by $x + 5$

AIM

Quadratic Loop Game B Sheet 2

F

$x^2 + 7x + 10$

Divide by $x + 2$
Multiply by $x - 1$

AIM

Quadratic Loop Game B Sheet 2

F

$x^2 + 4x - 5$

Divide by $x + 5$
Multiply by $x + 4$

AIM

Quadratic Loop Game B Sheet 2

F

$x + 3x - 4$

Divide by $x + 4$
Multiply by $x + 2$

AIM

Quadratic Loop Game B Sheet 2

F

$x^2 + x - 2$

Divide by $x - 1$
Multiply by $x + 3$

AIM

Quadratic Loop Game B Sheet 2

F

$x^2 + 5x + 6$

Divide by $x + 3$
Multiply by $x - 4$

AIM

Four in a Line

Introduction

Four in a line games can be designed to practise almost any algebraic skill. The ones presented here illustrate some of the possibilities.

Several possible forms of the rules are given, which adds variety to each game.

To avoid dissension, it is suggested that the game is **not** played with counters on the board as this can cause problems in reading formulae or other information from the board. When the board is moved to allow a player to see better, the counters inevitably move. The game should be played on a laminated copy of the board which can be written on with dry markers. Alternatively, the game can be played on a photocopy of the board and players can mark their progress on the board with a pen.

Four in a Line Rules

VERSION A: WHOLE CLASS

Play with the class grouped in teams in some way.

Project an OHP copy of the board onto a whiteboard, and cross off the captured rectangles or mark them with a small cube.

Each team in turn chooses two numbers/expressions from the resource set and carries out an operation to combine them. If the answer is on the board they capture that rectangle.

They score 1 point if the rectangle is not joined to any other rectangles already captured (by anyone). Otherwise they score a number of points equal to the number of rectangles in the block of captured rectangles of which the new rectangle forms part.

There is a further bonus point for anyone completing a line of four rectangles vertically, horizontally, or diagonally.

VERSION B: GROUPS

As above, but play on a photocopy so that the sheet can be moved about without losing the position.

VERSION C: PAIRS

Play like noughts and crosses on a photocopy of the board. The winner is the player who first gets four in a line.

VERSION D: PUZZLE - GROUP OR INDIVIDUAL

Determine whether all the rectangles on the board can be captured. Explain how each answer can be obtained. Some versions deliberately have one rectangle which cannot be captured!

Addition and Subtraction Four in a Line

Add or subtract two expressions from the top box. If the answer is on the grid and not already claimed, you win that rectangle.

$p+2q$	$2p+q$	$p-2q$
$2p-q$	$2p+2q$	$2p+3q$

$$+ \qquad -$$

$3p+3q$	$4q$	$p-q$	$4p-q$
$2q$	$p+3q$	$3p$	$4p+3q$
$p+4q$	$p-3q$	$3p-q$	$4p$
$3p-3q$	$p+q$	$4p-2q$	$3p-5q$
$3p+q$	$5q$	p	$3p-q$

Substitution Four in a Line

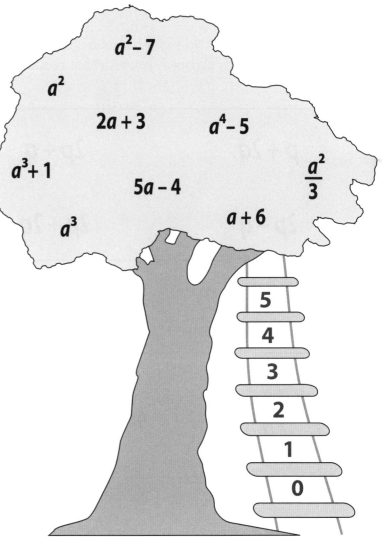

a^2-7

a^2

$2a+3$

a^4-5

a^3+1

$5a-4$

$\dfrac{a^2}{3}$

a^3

$a+6$

Specific Instructions

Work on a copy of the board below.

Version 1

Choose one of the numbers on the ladder by the tree and substitute it into a formula of your choice from the tree. If the answer is on the board and not already claimed, you win that rectangle.

Version 2

Throw a dice marked 0 to 5 to generate the number.

Otherwise as above.

–5	–4	–3	–2	–1
0	1	2	3	4
5	6	7	8	9
10	11	12	13	14
15	16	17	18	19

Three in a Line Rules

This game requires a blank dice that has been marked:

$x - 2$, $2x$, $-x$, x, $2x + 2$, $2x - 2$

and a copy of the board *Three in a Line*.

Players (preferably with each 'player' being a pair of pupils) take it in turns to throw the dice. They can then claim any rectangle on the board which contains an expression equivalent to the one on the dice.

Any player who wins three rectangles in a line, horizontally, vertically, or diagonally wins a point. The rectangles in this line may not be used in any other line.

Play continues until no more lines can be made.

The player with the highest number of points wins.

Three in a Line Board

$x+x$	$-(2-x)$	$1\times x$	$x\times-1$	$2(x-1)$	$2(x+1)$
$1\times x-2$	$2x-x$	$2\times x-2$	$2+2x$	$-1\times x$	$2x-(x+2)$
$2x+0\times x$	$6-(x+6)$	$4x-2x-2$	$6+3x-x-4$	$8+4x-10-3x$	$2x-x+2\times x$
$-2(1-x)$	$0-x$	$\dfrac{4x}{2}$	$3x-x$	$-2+x$	$(x+1)2$
$\dfrac{2x}{2}$	$x+x-2$	$x+0$	$1-(x+1)$	$2\times x$	$2(x-1)-x$
$x\times2$	$3x-x$	$x\times2+2$	$(x-1)\times2$	$x-2x$	$x+2+x$

Multiplication and Division Four in a Line

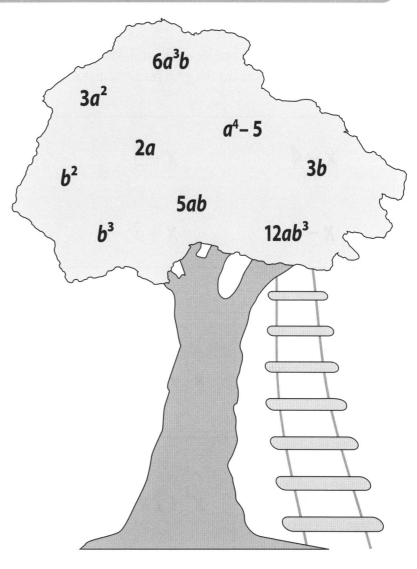

$6a^3b$

$3a^2$

$a^4 - 5$

$2a$

b^2

$3b$

$5ab$

b^3

$12ab^3$

Specific Instructions

Work on a copy of the board below.

Choose two of the formulae on the tree and either multiply or divide them. If the answer is on the board and not already claimed, you win that rectangle.

$2a^3$	$3b^3$	$5ab^3$	a^3b^3	$6b^3$
$6ab$	$72a^4b^4$	$12a^4b^3$	$2ab$	$2a^4$
$10a^2b$	$12a$	b	$2ab^2$	$3a^5$
$15ab^2$	$9a^2b$	$5a^4b$	$6b$	$10a^2$
$24a^2b^3$	$60a^2b^4$	$15ab^2$	$30a^4b^3$	$3a^2b$

Quadratic Four in a Line

Multiply two expressions from the top box. You can use the same expression twice. If the answer is on the grid and not already claimed, you win that rectangle.

$x-4$	$x+5$	$x-2$	$x+1$
$x-7$	$x+3$	$x-6$	$x+8$

x^2+x-20	x^2+9x+8	$x^2+2x-48$	$x^2-4x-21$
x^2-6x+8	x^2+2x+1	$x^2+3x-10$	$x^2-13x-42$
$x^2-2x-35$	$x^2-11x+28$	$x^2+10x+25$	x^2+6x+5
$x^2-9x+14$	$x^2-3x-18$	x^2+6x+9	x^2-5x-6
$x^2+4x-32$	x^2-4x+4	x^2-6x-7	$x^2-13x+42$

Target Games

Introduction

Games such as these can be modified to practise any level of algebraic skill. The four which are given here are just exemplars.

The rule which allows the exchange of a card is a crucial part of the mathematics as it requires the player to consider the properties of the expression on the card and whether it is likely to give a good score for the current target. The introduction of this rule, suggested by the pupils with whom I was researching algebraic games, changes this type of game from routine practice to one encouraging understanding and insight.

Linear Targets in particular is very interesting, despite its apparent simplicity, as it is often possible for a player to be sure whether or not they will win before the dice is thrown. On occasions the throw of the dice is unnecessary to determine the points to be scored. Also the pupils start to estimate probabilities of winning if the outcome is not sure.

Target Games Rules

Each game can be played either with a standard dice or a 1 to 8 dice or a 0 to 9 or a 1 to 10 dice. Each game can be made more complex by throwing a dice marked + + + − − − at the same time so that the inputs can be negative integers.

Negative Targets in particular was designed to be used with positive and negative inputs.

The game is best played by pairs of players acting as a team. Three pairs is a suitable number to play a game.

Separate the cards into formula cards (e.g. $2D + 1$) and target cards (e.g. the smallest number).

Shuffle the target cards and put them face down on the table.

Deal one formula card to each pair of players.

Put the rest of the cards face down on the table and turn up the top card to be an exposed card.

Place the target cards face down on the table.

At each turn a target card is turned up. The players then have a chance to exchange their formula card either for the exposed card or for the top card on the pile. The first opportunity to change the card should rotate round the players. **Only one change may be made by each pair in any one turn**. The dice is/are then thrown and this is the value of the letter in the formula card for all the pairs. The player(s) satisfying the target win(s) a point.

Play continues to any agreed finishing point e.g. the target cards have all been used once, or when a pair reach a given number of points.

If at any point either pile is exhausted it should be shuffled and replaced as at the start of the game.

Linear Targets

Formula Cards 1

Linear Targets Formula Cards 1

$$5n + 4$$

AIM

Linear Targets Formula Cards 1

$$6n - 2$$

AIM

Linear Targets Formula Cards 1

$$2n + 1$$

AIM

Linear Targets Formula Cards 1

$$6n$$

AIM

Linear Targets Formula Cards 1

$$6n - 5$$

AIM

Linear Targets Formula Cards 1

$$5n - 4$$

AIM

Linear Targets Formula Cards 1

$$6n + 3$$

AIM

Linear Targets Formula Cards 1

$$3n + 1$$

AIM

Linear Targets Formula Cards 1

$$5n + 3$$

AIM

Linear Targets Formula Cards 1

$$4n$$

AIM

Linear Targets Formula Cards 1

$$6n + 2$$

AIM

Linear Targets Formula Cards 1

$$5n$$

AIM

Linear Targets Formula Cards 1

$$6n + 4$$

AIM

Linear Targets Formula Cards 1

$$6n + 5$$

AIM

Linear Targets Formula Cards 1

$$4n - 2$$

AIM

Linear Targets Formula Cards 1

$$6n + 1$$

AIM

Linear Targets Formula Cards 1

$$6n - 3$$

AIM

Linear Targets Formula Cards 1

$$5n - 1$$

AIM

Linear Targets Formula Cards 2

$5n - 6$

AIM

Linear Targets Formula Cards 2

$5n - 2$

AIM

Linear Targets Formula Cards 2

$5n + 2$

AIM

Linear Targets Formula Cards 2

$3n - 1$

AIM

Linear Targets Formula Cards 2

$2n$

AIM

Linear Targets Formula Cards 2

$8n - 10$

AIM

Linear Targets Formula Cards 2

$6n - 1$

AIM

Linear Targets Formula Cards 2

$3n$

AIM

Linear Targets Formula Cards 2

$3n + 2$

AIM

Linear Targets Formula Cards 2

$2n - 3$

AIM

Linear Targets Formula Cards 2

$6n - 4$

AIM

Linear Targets Formula Cards 2

$4n + 2$

AIM

Linear Targets Formula Cards 2

$4n - 3$

AIM

Linear Targets Formula Cards 2

$4n + 3$

AIM

Linear Targets Formula Cards 2

$5n - 3$

AIM

Linear Targets Formula Cards 2

$4n - 1$

AIM

Linear Targets Formula Cards 2

$4n + 1$

AIM

Linear Targets Formula Cards 2

$5n + 1$

AIM

The biggest
number
AIM

The smallest
number
AIM

An even
number
AIM

A multiple
of 3
AIM

A multiple
of 5
AIM

A negative
number
AIM

The biggest
number
AIM

The smallest
number
AIM

An even
number
AIM

An odd
number
AIM

Nearest
to 5
AIM

Not a
multiple of 3
AIM

A number
greater than 9
AIM

Nearest
to zero
AIM

One more than
a multiple of 3
AIM

A number
less than 5
AIM

Between 2
and 4
inclusive
AIM

Not a whole
number
AIM

Easier Targets Formula Cards 1

$$4 - 2D$$

ATM

Easier Targets Formula Cards 1

$$6(D - 2)$$

ATM

Easier Targets Formula Cards 1

$$2(D + 1)$$

ATM

Easier Targets Formula Cards 1

$$10 - 6D$$

ATM

Easier Targets Formula Cards 1

$$6D + 5$$

ATM

Easier Targets Formula Cards 1

$$\frac{12}{D}$$

ATM

Easier Targets Formula Cards 1

$$\frac{D + 1}{2}$$

ATM

Easier Targets Formula Cards 1

$$3D - 7$$

ATM

Easier Targets Formula Cards 1

$$5D + 4$$

ATM

Easier Targets Formula Cards 1

$$\frac{D}{4}$$

ATM

Easier Targets Formula Cards 1

$$6(D + 2)$$

ATM

Easier Targets Formula Cards 1

$$5 - D$$

ATM

Easier Targets Formula Cards 1

$$6D - 8$$

ATM

Easier Targets Formula Cards 1

$$6(D + 5)$$

ATM

Easier Targets Formula Cards 1

$$4(2 - D)$$

ATM

Easier Targets Formula Cards 1

$$\frac{D + 1}{6}$$

ATM

Easier Targets Formula Cards 1

$$6(D - 3)$$

ATM

Easier Targets Formula Cards 1

$$1 - 5D$$

ATM

Easier Targets Formula Cards 2

$$6 - 5D$$

ATM

Easier Targets Formula Cards 2

$$5(D - 3)$$

ATM

Easier Targets Formula Cards 2

$$\frac{D + 5}{2}$$

ATM

Easier Targets Formula Cards 2

$$8 - 3D$$

ATM

Easier Targets Formula Cards 2

$$\frac{8}{D}$$

ATM

Easier Targets Formula Cards 2

$$8(D - 1)$$

ATM

Easier Targets Formula Cards 2

$$6(D - 2)$$

ATM

Easier Targets Formula Cards 2

$$12 - 3D$$

ATM

Easier Targets Formula Cards 2

$$\frac{2D}{3}$$

ATM

Easier Targets Formula Cards 2

$$2(3 - D)$$

ATM

Easier Targets Formula Cards 2

$$6D - 8$$

ATM

Easier Targets Formula Cards 2

$$\frac{4D}{5}$$

ATM

Easier Targets Formula Cards 2

$$4(D - 3)$$

ATM

Easier Targets Formula Cards 2

$$4D + 5$$

ATM

Easier Targets Formula Cards 2

$$13 - 5D$$

ATM

Easier Targets Formula Cards 2

$$\frac{20}{D}$$

ATM

Easier Targets Formula Cards 2

$$4(D + 1)$$

ATM

Easier Targets Formula Cards 2

$$10 - 5D$$

ATM

Easier Targets Target Cards
The biggest number
AIM

Easier Targets Target Cards
The smallest number
AIM

Easier Targets Target Cards
A whole number
AIM

Easier Targets Target Cards
A number greater than 5
AIM

Easier Targets Target Cards
A number between 1 and 7 inclusive
AIM

Easier Targets Target Cards
A negative number
AIM

Easier Targets Target Cards
The biggest number
AIM

Easier Targets Target Cards
The smallest number
AIM

Easier Targets Target Cards
Nearest to −3
AIM

Easier Targets Target Cards
Nearest to zero
AIM

Easier Targets Target Cards
Nearest to 5
AIM

Easier Targets Target Cards
Not a whole number
AIM

Easier Targets Target Cards
A number greater than 9
AIM

Easier Targets Target Cards
A number less than −2
AIM

Easier Targets Target Cards
A number less than −5
AIM

Easier Targets Target Cards
A number less than 5
AIM

Easier Targets Target Cards
Between −2 and 2 inclusive
AIM

Easier Targets Target Cards
A whole number
AIM

Negative Targets

Formula Cards 1

$$2D + 1$$
ATM

$$2(D + 3)$$
ATM

$$3D - 1$$
ATM

$$3(D + 4)$$
ATM

$$5 - D$$
ATM

$$10 - D$$
ATM

$$12 - 2D$$
ATM

$$12 - 3D$$
ATM

$$\frac{D}{2} + 4$$
ATM

$$\frac{D}{2} - 7$$
ATM

$$5(D - 3)$$
ATM

$$5D + 1$$
ATM

$$2D + 4$$
ATM

$$3D - 6$$
ATM

$$5D - 10$$
ATM

$$\frac{D}{3} + 7$$
ATM

$$\frac{D}{3} - 2$$
ATM

$$\frac{D}{2} + 4$$
ATM

Negative Targets Formula Cards 2

$$\frac{D-4}{2}$$

ATM

Negative Targets Formula Cards 2

$$\frac{D+1}{10}$$

ATM

Negative Targets Formula Cards 2

$$\frac{D-1}{10}$$

ATM

Negative Targets Formula Cards 2

$$2(10-D)$$

ATM

Negative Targets Formula Cards 2

$$2(11-D)$$

ATM

Negative Targets Formula Cards 2

$$3(5-D)$$

ATM

Negative Targets Formula Cards 2

$$3(2-D)$$

ATM

Negative Targets Formula Cards 2

$$\frac{2D+1}{2}$$

ATM

Negative Targets Formula Cards 2

$$\frac{4D+2}{2}$$

ATM

Negative Targets Formula Cards 2

$$\frac{3D+6}{3}$$

ATM

Negative Targets Formula Cards 2

$$\frac{3D-3}{3}$$

ATM

Negative Targets Formula Cards 2

$$2D+3$$

ATM

Negative Targets Formula Cards 2

$$3D-9$$

ATM

Negative Targets Formula Cards 2

$$5D+1$$

ATM

Negative Targets Formula Cards 2

$$5D-3$$

ATM

Negative Targets Formula Cards 2

$$2(10-4D)$$

ATM

Negative Targets Formula Cards 2

$$3(10+D)$$

ATM

Negative Targets Formula Cards 2

$$5(10-D)$$

ATM

Negative Targets Target Cards

The biggest number

ATM

Negative Targets Target Cards

The smallest number

ATM

Negative Targets Target Cards

An even number

ATM

Negative Targets Target Cards

A multiple of 3

ATM

Negative Targets Target Cards

A multiple of 5

ATM

Negative Targets Target Cards

A negative number

ATM

Negative Targets Target Cards

The biggest number

ATM

Negative Targets Target Cards

The smallest number

ATM

Negative Targets Target Cards

Between −2 and 2

ATM

Negative Targets Target Cards

An odd number

ATM

Negative Targets Target Cards

Nearest to 5

ATM

Negative Targets Target Cards

Nearest to −2

ATM

Negative Targets Target Cards

A number greater than 9

ATM

Negative Targets Target Cards

Nearest to zero

ATM

Negative Targets Target Cards

Nearest to −1

ATM

Negative Targets Target Cards

A number less than −2

ATM

Negative Targets Target Cards

Between −3 and 0

ATM

Negative Targets Target Cards

Between 1 and 6

ATM

Quadratic Targets

Quadratic Targets Formula Cards 1

$$n^2 + 2$$

Quadratic Targets Formula Cards 1

$$\frac{n^2}{4}$$

Quadratic Targets Formula Cards 1

$$\left(\frac{n}{9}\right)^2$$

Quadratic Targets Formula Cards 1

$$n^2 + 2n + 3$$

Quadratic Targets Formula Cards 1

$$n^2 + 7$$

Quadratic Targets Formula Cards 1

$$n^2 + 2n + 7$$

Quadratic Targets Formula Cards 1

$$n^2 - 7$$

Quadratic Targets Formula Cards 1

$$2n^2 + 7$$

Quadratic Targets Formula Cards 1

$$\frac{n^2 - 1}{9}$$

Quadratic Targets Formula Cards 1

$$(2n)^2 + 7$$

Quadratic Targets Formula Cards 1

$$(n - 4)^2$$

Quadratic Targets Formula Cards 1

$$3n^2 + 1$$

Quadratic Targets Formula Cards 1

$$3n^2 - 1$$

Quadratic Targets Formula Cards 1

$$\left(\frac{n}{5}\right)^2 - 2$$

Quadratic Targets Formula Cards 1

$$\left(\frac{n}{3}\right)^2 - 6$$

Quadratic Targets Formula Cards 1

$$\left(\frac{n}{5}\right)^2 + 3$$

Quadratic Targets Formula Cards 1

$$\left(\frac{n}{4}\right)^2 - 2$$

Quadratic Targets Formula Cards 1

$$(n - 5)^2$$

Quadratic Targets

Formula Cards 2

Quadratic Targets Formula Cards 2

$$\left(\frac{n}{8}\right)^2 + 4$$

AIM

Quadratic Targets Formula Cards 2

$$(n+3)^2$$

AIM

Quadratic Targets Formula Cards 2

$$\left(\frac{n}{8}\right)^2 + 4$$

AIM

Quadratic Targets Formula Cards 2

$$n^2 + 3$$

AIM

Quadratic Targets Formula Cards 2

$$3n^2 + 3$$

AIM

Quadratic Targets Formula Cards 2

$$3n^2 + 3n + 3$$

AIM

Quadratic Targets Formula Cards 2

$$(3n)^2 + 3$$

AIM

Quadratic Targets Formula Cards 2

$$\frac{2n^2 - 1}{9}$$

AIM

Quadratic Targets Formula Cards 2

$$\frac{2n^2 + 1}{9}$$

AIM

Quadratic Targets Formula Cards 2

$$\frac{2n^2 + n - 1}{9}$$

AIM

Quadratic Targets Formula Cards 2

$$\frac{(2n - 1)^2}{9}$$

AIM

Quadratic Targets Formula Cards 2

$$\frac{n^2 - 4}{3}$$

AIM

Quadratic Targets Formula Cards 2

$$\frac{(n - 4)^2}{9}$$

AIM

Quadratic Targets Formula Cards 2

$$20 - n^2$$

AIM

Quadratic Targets Formula Cards 2

$$n^2 - 20$$

AIM

Quadratic Targets Formula Cards 2

$$50 - 2n^2$$

AIM

Quadratic Targets Formula Cards 2

$$50 - (2n)^2$$

AIM

Quadratic Targets Formula Cards 2

$$(2n)^2 - 50$$

AIM

Quadratic Targets

The biggest number

ATM

The smallest number

ATM

An even number

ATM

A multiple of 3

ATM

Greater than 30

ATM

A negative number

ATM

The biggest number

ATM

The smallest number

ATM

Between 0 and 2

ATM

An odd number

ATM

Nearest to 5

ATM

Nearest to −2

ATM

A number greater than 9

ATM

Nearest to zero

ATM

Nearest to −1

ATM

A number less than −2

ATM

Between 3 and 6

ATM

Between 5 and 10

ATM

Equation Card Games

Introduction

When the easiest form of these games is first played, all the pupils need to be told is that they have to discover whether their dice throw yields a number which satisfies the equation. The children then devise their own procedures for solving the equations. Quite soon one hears comments like 'I need a 3 and two 6s'. Peer tuition often takes place, but the game allows the less confident player to 'hide' and just use substitution methods until they feel more secure.

Even when 'two-sided' equations are reached many pupils devise their own strategies such as writing

$2x + 21 = 5x$ as $2x + 3 \times 7 = 5x$ and   deduce that $x = 7$.

The games shown illustrate the wide range of equations which can be used in this game.

Equation Card Games Rules

THESE GAMES ARE BEST PLAYED BY FOUR INDIVIDUALS OR SIX PLAYERS PLAYING IN PAIRS

You will need a dice showing the solutions used in the equations on its faces. For the second quadratic equation game you will need a dice marked with three + signs and three – signs together with a standard dice.

Deal two cards to each player. It can be valuable to play this in pairs, in which case each player in the pair has two cards but they co-operate in playing. Put the remainder of the cards face down on the table.

The dice is thrown and each throw applies to all players. Each player wins any card whose root is the score on the dice. The player must get an opponent to agree to the solution. Any card won is replaced from the pile.

When the pile is exhausted the players may win their remaining cards by stating their solutions.

As the players become more confident three cards may be dealt to each player.

Simple Equation Game

Solutions 1 to 8.

$$2x + 1 = 3$$

ATM

$$4x - 2 = 2$$

ATM

$$5x - 2 = 3$$

ATM

$$3x + 2 = 5$$

ATM

$$5x + 1 = 6$$

ATM

$$4x - 5 = 3$$

ATM

$$7x - 10 = 4$$

ATM

$$3x + 2 = 8$$

ATM

$$8x - 6 = 10$$

ATM

$$3x - 2 = 7$$

ATM

$$2x + 1 = 7$$

ATM

$$5x - 1 = 14$$

ATM

$$4x - 2 = 10$$

ATM

$$6x - 10 = 8$$

ATM

$$2x + 1 = 9$$

ATM

$$3x - 2 = 10$$

ATM

$$5x + 1 = 21$$

ATM

$$6x - 4 = 20$$

ATM

Simple Equation Game

Solutions 1 to 8.

Simple Equation Game Solutions 1 to 8 Sheet 2

$5x - 10 = 15$

AIM

Simple Equation Game Solutions 1 to 8 Sheet 2

$2x + 1 = 11$

AIM

Simple Equation Game Solutions 1 to 8 Sheet 2

$3x - 2 = 13$

AIM

Simple Equation Game Solutions 1 to 8 Sheet 2

$3x - 9 = 6$

AIM

Simple Equation Game Solutions 1 to 8 Sheet 2

$2x - 1 = 11$

AIM

Simple Equation Game Solutions 1 to 8 Sheet 2

$2x + 1 = 13$

AIM

Simple Equation Game Solutions 1 to 8 Sheet 2

$3x - 10 = 8$

AIM

Simple Equation Game Solutions 1 to 8 Sheet 2

$4x + 6 = 30$

AIM

Simple Equation Game Solutions 1 to 8 Sheet 2

$5x - 1 = 29$

AIM

Simple Equation Game Solutions 1 to 8 Sheet 2

$x - 1 = 6$

AIM

Simple Equation Game Solutions 1 to 8 Sheet 2

$2x + 1 = 11$

AIM

Simple Equation Game Solutions 1 to 8 Sheet 2

$2x - 3 = 11$

AIM

Simple Equation Game Solutions 1 to 8 Sheet 2

$3x - 1 = 20$

AIM

Simple Equation Game Solutions 1 to 8 Sheet 2

$4x + 2 = 30$

AIM

Simple Equation Game Solutions 1 to 8 Sheet 2

$3x - 2 = 22$

AIM

Simple Equation Game Solutions 1 to 8 Sheet 2

$4x + 1 = 33$

AIM

Simple Equation Game Solutions 1 to 8 Sheet 2

$2x - 1 = 15$

AIM

Simple Equation Game Solutions 1 to 8 Sheet 2

$5x - 2 = 38$

AIM

Equation Game – Variable Letters

Solutions 0, 2, 3, 5, 6, 7.

Equation Game Variable Letters Sheet 1

$$4N + 2 = 2$$

ATM

Equation Game Variable Letters Sheet 1

$$8T + 1 = 1$$

ATM

Equation Game Variable Letters Sheet 1

$$\frac{T}{3} + 5 = 5$$

ATM

Equation Game Variable Letters Sheet 1

$$\frac{2D + 6}{2} = 3$$

ATM

Equation Game Variable Letters Sheet 1

$$3(P + 2) = 6$$

ATM

Equation Game Variable Letters Sheet 1

$$4(Q + 1) = 4$$

ATM

Equation Game Variable Letters Sheet 1

$$6N - 1 = 11$$

ATM

Equation Game Variable Letters Sheet 1

$$6(N - 1) = 6$$

ATM

Equation Game Variable Letters Sheet 1

$$\frac{D}{2} + 3 = 4$$

ATM

Equation Game Variable Letters Sheet 1

$$\frac{2Q + 2}{2} = 3$$

ATM

Equation Game Variable Letters Sheet 1

$$2(G + 3) = 10$$

ATM

Equation Game Variable Letters Sheet 1

$$5Q - 3 = 7$$

ATM

Equation Game Variable Letters Sheet 1

$$4x + 1 = 13$$

ATM

Equation Game Variable Letters Sheet 1

$$5x - 10 = 5$$

ATM

Equation Game Variable Letters Sheet 1

$$2(x - 2) = 2$$

ATM

Equation Game Variable Letters Sheet 1

$$\frac{Q}{3} + 4 = 5$$

ATM

Equation Game Variable Letters Sheet 1

$$\frac{x + 1}{2} = 2$$

ATM

Equation Game Variable Letters Sheet 1

$$3(y - 1) = 6$$

ATM

Equation Game – Variable Letters   Sheet 2

Solutions 0, 2, 3, 5, 6, 7.

Equation Game Variable Letters Sheet 2

$$\frac{Q}{5} + 2 = 3$$

AIM

Equation Game Variable Letters Sheet 2

$$\frac{3Q + 1}{4} = 4$$

AIM

Equation Game Variable Letters Sheet 2

$$2P + 3 = 13$$

AIM

Equation Game Variable Letters Sheet 2

$$2(T - 3) = 4$$

AIM

Equation Game Variable Letters Sheet 2

$$4D - 2 = 18$$

AIM

Equation Game Variable Letters Sheet 2

$$6(T - 3) = 12$$

AIM

Equation Game Variable Letters Sheet 2

$$\frac{X}{2} - 1 = 2$$

AIM

Equation Game Variable Letters Sheet 2

$$\frac{Q + 2}{4} = 2$$

AIM

Equation Game Variable Letters Sheet 2

$$3P + 2 = 20$$

AIM

Equation Game Variable Letters Sheet 2

$$\frac{X}{3} + 2 = 4$$

AIM

Equation Game Variable Letters Sheet 2

$$2(y - 3) = 6$$

AIM

Equation Game Variable Letters Sheet 2

$$5(x - 4) = 10$$

AIM

Equation Game Variable Letters Sheet 2

$$2(D - 1) = 12$$

AIM

Equation Game Variable Letters Sheet 2

$$2N - 4 = 10$$

AIM

Equation Game Variable Letters Sheet 2

$$3N - 1 = 20$$

AIM

Equation Game Variable Letters Sheet 2

$$\frac{D + 1}{2} = 4$$

AIM

Equation Game Variable Letters Sheet 2

$$3(N - 5) = 6$$

AIM

Equation Game Variable Letters Sheet 2

$$3(Q - 1) = 18$$

AIM

Hard Equation Game

Solutions 0 to 9.

Hard Equation Game Solutions 0 to 9 Sheet 1

$$\frac{20}{x} + 1 = 5$$

ATM

Hard Equation Game Solutions 0 to 9 Sheet 1

$$2(12 - 2x) = 4$$

ATM

Hard Equation Game Solutions 0 to 9 Sheet 1

$$\frac{15}{x - 2} = 5$$

ATM

Hard Equation Game Solutions 0 to 9 Sheet 1

$$x^2 - 10 = 15$$

ATM

Hard Equation Game Solutions 0 to 9 Sheet 1

$$3(7 - x) = 6$$

ATM

Hard Equation Game Solutions 0 to 9 Sheet 1

$$\frac{24}{x} + 1 = 5$$

ATM

Hard Equation Game Solutions 0 to 9 Sheet 1

$$\frac{24}{x + 2} = 3$$

ATM

Hard Equation Game Solutions 0 to 9 Sheet 1

$$x^2 - 20 = 16$$

ATM

Hard Equation Game Solutions 0 to 9 Sheet 1

$$3(22 - 3x) = 3$$

ATM

Hard Equation Game Solutions 0 to 9 Sheet 1

$$\frac{18}{x - 1} = 3$$

ATM

Hard Equation Game Solutions 0 to 9 Sheet 1

$$\frac{14}{x} + 4 = 6$$

ATM

Hard Equation Game Solutions 0 to 9 Sheet 1

$$x^2 + 1 = 50$$

ATM

Hard Equation Game Solutions 0 to 9 Sheet 1

$$\frac{16}{x} + 5 = 7$$

ATM

Hard Equation Game Solutions 0 to 9 Sheet 1

$$\frac{40}{x + 2} = 4$$

ATM

Hard Equation Game Solutions 0 to 9 Sheet 1

$$3(9 - x) = 3$$

ATM

Hard Equation Game Solutions 0 to 9 Sheet 1

$$x^2 - 50 = 14$$

ATM

Hard Equation Game Solutions 0 to 9 Sheet 1

$$\frac{18}{x} + 2 = 4$$

ATM

Hard Equation Game Solutions 0 to 9 Sheet 1

$$\frac{20}{x + 1} = 2$$

ATM

Hard Equation Game

Solutions 0 to 9.

Hard Equation Game Solutions 0 to 9 Sheet 2

$$3(2 - x) = 3$$

ATM

Hard Equation Game Solutions 0 to 9 Sheet 2

$$\frac{4}{x} + 3 = 7$$

ATM

Hard Equation Game Solutions 0 to 9 Sheet 2

$$2(5 + 3x) = 16$$

ATM

Hard Equation Game Solutions 0 to 9 Sheet 2

$$x^2 + 5 = 6$$

ATM

Hard Equation Game Solutions 0 to 9 Sheet 2

$$8(5 - x) = 24$$

ATM

Hard Equation Game Solutions 0 to 9 Sheet 2

$$\frac{10}{x} - 1 = 4$$

ATM

Hard Equation Game Solutions 0 to 9 Sheet 2

$$3(1 + 3x) = 21$$

ATM

Hard Equation Game Solutions 0 to 9 Sheet 2

$$x^2 - 1 = 3$$

ATM

Hard Equation Game Solutions 0 to 9 Sheet 2

$$5(12 - 3x) = 15$$

ATM

Hard Equation Game Solutions 0 to 9 Sheet 2

$$\frac{24}{x} - 3 = 5$$

ATM

Hard Equation Game Solutions 0 to 9 Sheet 2

$$4(1 + 2x) = 28$$

ATM

Hard Equation Game Solutions 0 to 9 Sheet 2

$$x^2 + 1 = 10$$

ATM

Hard Equation Game Solutions 0 to 9 Sheet 2

$$2(8 - x) = 8$$

ATM

Hard Equation Game Solutions 0 to 9 Sheet 2

$$\frac{8}{x} - 1 = 1$$

ATM

Hard Equation Game Solutions 0 to 9 Sheet 2

$$\frac{12}{x + 2} = 2$$

ATM

Hard Equation Game Solutions 0 to 9 Sheet 2

$$x^2 - 6 = 10$$

ATM

Hard Equation Game Solutions 0 to 9 Sheet 2

$$4(2 + 7x) = 8$$

ATM

Hard Equation Game Solutions 0 to 9 Sheet 2

$$3(8 - 7x) = 24$$

ATM

Equation Cards – Negative Solutions   Sheet 1

Solutions −1 to −6.

Equation Cards – Negative Solutions Sheet 1

$$2x + 3 = 1$$

ATM

Equation Cards – Negative Solutions Sheet 1

$$3x + 7 = 4$$

ATM

Equation Cards – Negative Solutions Sheet 1

$$4x + 10 = 6$$

ATM

Equation Cards – Negative Solutions Sheet 1

$$\frac{x + 3}{2} = 1$$

ATM

Equation Cards – Negative Solutions Sheet 1

$$\frac{x + 10}{3} = 3$$

ATM

Equation Cards – Negative Solutions Sheet 1

$$2(x + 2) = 2$$

ATM

Equation Cards – Negative Solutions Sheet 1

$$2x + 7 = 3$$

ATM

Equation Cards – Negative Solutions Sheet 1

$$3x + 10 = 4$$

ATM

Equation Cards – Negative Solutions Sheet 1

$$4x + 15 = 7$$

ATM

Equation Cards – Negative Solutions Sheet 1

$$\frac{x + 5}{3} = 1$$

ATM

Equation Cards – Negative Solutions Sheet 1

$$\frac{2x + 4}{7} = 0$$

ATM

Equation Cards – Negative Solutions Sheet 1

$$\frac{2x + 10}{3} = 2$$

ATM

Equation Cards – Negative Solutions Sheet 1

$$2(x + 5) = 4$$

ATM

Equation Cards – Negative Solutions Sheet 1

$$2x + 8 = 2$$

ATM

Equation Cards – Negative Solutions Sheet 1

$$3x + 10 = 1$$

ATM

Equation Cards – Negative Solutions Sheet 1

$$5x + 20 = 5$$

ATM

Equation Cards – Negative Solutions Sheet 1

$$3(x + 4) = 3$$

ATM

Equation Cards – Negative Solutions Sheet 1

$$\frac{x + 5}{2} = 1$$

ATM

Equation Cards – Negative Solutions — Sheet 2

Solutions −1 to −6.

Equation Cards – Negative Solutions Sheet 2

$$2x + 10 = 2$$

ATM

Equation Cards – Negative Solutions Sheet 2

$$\frac{x}{2} + 3 = 1$$

ATM

Equation Cards – Negative Solutions Sheet 2

$$3x + 14 = 2$$

ATM

Equation Cards – Negative Solutions Sheet 2

$$2(x + 6) = 4$$

ATM

Equation Cards – Negative Solutions Sheet 2

$$3(x + 7) = 9$$

ATM

Equation Cards – Negative Solutions Sheet 2

$$\frac{x + 6}{2} = 1$$

ATM

Equation Cards – Negative Solutions Sheet 2

$$2x + 11 = 1$$

ATM

Equation Cards – Negative Solutions Sheet 2

$$2x + 20 = 10$$

ATM

Equation Cards – Negative Solutions Sheet 2

$$3x + 20 = 5$$

ATM

Equation Cards – Negative Solutions Sheet 2

$$2(x + 7) = 4$$

ATM

Equation Cards – Negative Solutions Sheet 2

$$3(x + 8) = 9$$

ATM

Equation Cards – Negative Solutions Sheet 2

$$\frac{x + 10}{5} = 1$$

ATM

Equation Cards – Negative Solutions Sheet 2

$$2x + 15 = 3$$

ATM

Equation Cards – Negative Solutions Sheet 2

$$2(x + 9) = 6$$

ATM

Equation Cards – Negative Solutions Sheet 2

$$3(x + 7) = 3$$

ATM

Equation Cards – Negative Solutions Sheet 2

$$\frac{x}{2} + 4 = 1$$

ATM

Equation Cards – Negative Solutions Sheet 2

$$\frac{x}{3} + 4 = 2$$

ATM

Equation Cards – Negative Solutions Sheet 2

$$\frac{x + 12}{2} = 3$$

ATM

Two Sided Equations

Sheet 1

Solutions 5 to 10.

Two Sided Equations Solutions 5 to 10 Sheet 1

$$2x = x + 5$$

ATM

Two Sided Equations Solutions 5 to 10 Sheet 1

$$3x = x + 10$$

ATM

Two Sided Equations Solutions 5 to 10 Sheet 1

$$4x + 5 = 5x$$

ATM

Two Sided Equations Solutions 5 to 10 Sheet 1

$$3x + 10 = 5x$$

ATM

Two Sided Equations Solutions 5 to 10 Sheet 1

$$6x = 3x + 15$$

ATM

Two Sided Equations Solutions 5 to 10 Sheet 1

$$7x = 5x + 10$$

ATM

Two Sided Equations Solutions 5 to 10 Sheet 1

$$4x = 3x + 6$$

ATM

Two Sided Equations Solutions 5 to 10 Sheet 1

$$4x = 2x + 12$$

ATM

Two Sided Equations Solutions 5 to 10 Sheet 1

$$6x = 5x + 6$$

ATM

Two Sided Equations Solutions 5 to 10 Sheet 1

$$x + 18 = 4x$$

ATM

Two Sided Equations Solutions 5 to 10 Sheet 1

$$10x = 8x + 12$$

ATM

Two Sided Equations Solutions 5 to 10 Sheet 1

$$11x = 10x + 6$$

ATM

Two Sided Equations Solutions 5 to 10 Sheet 1

$$3x = 2x + 7$$

ATM

Two Sided Equations Solutions 5 to 10 Sheet 1

$$4x = 2x + 14$$

ATM

Two Sided Equations Solutions 5 to 10 Sheet 1

$$3x + 7 = 4x$$

ATM

Two Sided Equations Solutions 5 to 10 Sheet 1

$$2x + 21 = 5x$$

ATM

Two Sided Equations Solutions 5 to 10 Sheet 1

$$8x = 7x + 7$$

ATM

Two Sided Equations Solutions 5 to 10 Sheet 1

$$3x + 14 = 5x$$

ATM

Solutions 5 to 10.

Two Sided Equations Solutions 5 to 10 Sheet 2	Two Sided Equations Solutions 5 to 10 Sheet 2	Two Sided Equations Solutions 5 to 10 Sheet 2
$3x + 8 = 4x$	$3x + 16 = 5x$	$7x = 6x + 8$
ATM	ATM	ATM
Two Sided Equations Solutions 5 to 10 Sheet 2	Two Sided Equations Solutions 5 to 10 Sheet 2	Two Sided Equations Solutions 5 to 10 Sheet 2
$2x + 16 = 4x$	$10x = 8x + 16$	$10x = 6x + 32$
ATM	ATM	ATM
Two Sided Equations Solutions 5 to 10 Sheet 2	Two Sided Equations Solutions 5 to 10 Sheet 2	Two Sided Equations Solutions 5 to 10 Sheet 2
$x + 9 = 2x$	$3x + 9 = 4x$	$5x = 3x + 18$
ATM	ATM	ATM
Two Sided Equations Solutions 5 to 10 Sheet 2	Two Sided Equations Solutions 5 to 10 Sheet 2	Two Sided Equations Solutions 5 to 10 Sheet 2
$6x + 18 = 8x$	$10x = 8x + 18$	$3x + 27 = 6x$
ATM	ATM	ATM
Two Sided Equations Solutions 5 to 10 Sheet 2	Two Sided Equations Solutions 5 to 10 Sheet 2	Two Sided Equations Solutions 5 to 10 Sheet 2
$2x = x + 10$	$5x + 10 = 6x$	$7x + 20 = 9x$
ATM	ATM	ATM
Two Sided Equations Solutions 5 to 10 Sheet 2	Two Sided Equations Solutions 5 to 10 Sheet 2	Two Sided Equations Solutions 5 to 10 Sheet 2
$11x = 9x + 20$	$3x + 30 = 6x$	$4x + 30 = 7x$
ATM	ATM	ATM

Equation Cards Fractional Solutions   Sheet 1

Solutions are 2¼, 2½, 2¾, 3¼, 3½, 3¾.

$$4x - 1 = 8$$

ATM

$$\frac{4x + 3}{4} = 3$$

ATM

$$\frac{4x}{3} = 3$$

ATM

$$4x + 9 = 18$$

ATM

$$8x + 1 = 19$$

ATM

$$12x - 1 = 26$$

ATM

$$2x + 8 = 13$$

ATM

$$2x - 1 = 4$$

ATM

$$2x + 1 = 6$$

ATM

$$\frac{4x}{5} + 1 = 3$$

ATM

$$\frac{2x}{5} = 1$$

ATM

$$8x - 7 = 13$$

ATM

$$4x - 1 = 10$$

ATM

$$4x + 5 = 16$$

ATM

$$\frac{4x}{11} = 1$$

ATM

$$8x - 11 = 11$$

ATM

$$\frac{4x + 5}{8} = 2$$

ATM

$$8x + 10 = 32$$

ATM

Equation Cards Fractional Solutions

Sheet 2

Solutions are 2¼, 2½, 2¾, 3¼, 3½, 3¾.

Equation Cards Fractional Solutions Sheet 2

$$4x - 1 = 12$$

ATM

Equation Cards Fractional Solutions Sheet 2

$$\frac{4x + 1}{7} = 2$$

ATM

Equation Cards Fractional Solutions Sheet 2

$$\frac{4x - 1}{3} = 4$$

ATM

Equation Cards Fractional Solutions Sheet 2

$$4x + 8 = 21$$

ATM

Equation Cards Fractional Solutions Sheet 2

$$8x + 7 = 33$$

ATM

Equation Cards Fractional Solutions Sheet 2

$$12x - 7 = 32$$

ATM

Equation Cards Fractional Solutions Sheet 2

$$2x + 3 = 10$$

ATM

Equation Cards Fractional Solutions Sheet 2

$$2x + 4 = 11$$

ATM

Equation Cards Fractional Solutions Sheet 2

$$\frac{2x + 7}{2} = 7$$

ATM

Equation Cards Fractional Solutions Sheet 2

$$\frac{2x + 1}{8} = 1$$

ATM

Equation Cards Fractional Solutions Sheet 2

$$\frac{2x}{7} = 1$$

ATM

Equation Cards Fractional Solutions Sheet 2

$$8x - 9 = 19$$

ATM

Equation Cards Fractional Solutions Sheet 2

$$4x - 7 = 8$$

ATM

Equation Cards Fractional Solutions Sheet 2

$$4x + 1 = 16$$

ATM

Equation Cards Fractional Solutions Sheet 2

$$\frac{4x + 5}{4} = 5$$

ATM

Equation Cards Fractional Solutions Sheet 2

$$8x - 19 = 11$$

ATM

Equation Cards Fractional Solutions Sheet 2

$$\frac{4x - 2}{13} = 1$$

ATM

Equation Cards Fractional Solutions Sheet 2

$$12x - 13 = 32$$

ATM

Quadratic Equation Game Roots 1 to 6

(Use 2 copies)

Quadratic Equation Game Roots 1 to 6

$$x^2-2x+1=0$$

ATM

Quadratic Equation Game Roots 1 to 6

$$x^2-3x+2=0$$

ATM

Quadratic Equation Game Roots 1 to 6

$$x^2-4x+3=0$$

ATM

Quadratic Equation Game Roots 1 to 6

$$x^2-5x+4=0$$

ATM

Quadratic Equation Game Roots 1 to 6

$$x^2-6x+5=0$$

ATM

Quadratic Equation Game Roots 1 to 6

$$x^2-7x+6=0$$

ATM

Quadratic Equation Game Roots 1 to 6

$$x^2-4x+4=0$$

ATM

Quadratic Equation Game Roots 1 to 6

$$x^2-5x+6=0$$

ATM

Quadratic Equation Game Roots 1 to 6

$$x^2-6x+8=0$$

ATM

Quadratic Equation Game Roots 1 to 6

$$x^2-7x+10=0$$

ATM

Quadratic Equation Game Roots 1 to 6

$$x^2-8x+12=0$$

ATM

Quadratic Equation Game Roots 1 to 6

$$x^2-7x+12=0$$

ATM

Quadratic Equation Game Roots 1 to 6

$$x^2-8x+15=0$$

ATM

Quadratic Equation Game Roots 1 to 6

$$x^2-9x+18=0$$

ATM

Quadratic Equation Game Roots 1 to 6

$$x^2-9x+20=0$$

ATM

Quadratic Equation Game Roots 1 to 6

$$x^2-10x+24=0$$

ATM

Quadratic Equation Game Roots 1 to 6

$$x^2-11x+30=0$$

ATM

Quadratic Equation Game Roots 1 to 6

$$x^2-12x+36=0$$

ATM

Quadratic Equation Game

Sheet 1

Roots ±1 to ±6

Quadratic Equation Game Roots ±1 to ±6 Sheet 1

$$x^2+4x-5=0$$

AIM

Quadratic Equation Game Roots ±1 to ±6 Sheet 1

$$x^2-10x+24=0$$

AIM

Quadratic Equation Game Roots ±1 to ±6 Sheet 1

$$x^2-x-6=0$$

AIM

Quadratic Equation Game Roots ±1 to ±6 Sheet 1

$$x^2-2x-3=0$$

AIM

Quadratic Equation Game Roots ±1 to ±6 Sheet 1

$$x^2-3x+2=0$$

AIM

Quadratic Equation Game Roots ±1 to ±6 Sheet 1

$$x^2-2x-8=0$$

AIM

Quadratic Equation Game Roots ±1 to ±6 Sheet 1

$$x^2+7x+12=0$$

AIM

Quadratic Equation Game Roots ±1 to ±6 Sheet 1

$$x^2-2x-15=0$$

AIM

Quadratic Equation Game Roots ±1 to ±6 Sheet 1

$$x^2+4x-5=0$$

AIM

Quadratic Equation Game Roots ±1 to ±6 Sheet 1

$$x^2-11x+30=0$$

AIM

Quadratic Equation Game Roots ±1 to ±6 Sheet 1

$$x^2-9x+20=0$$

AIM

Quadratic Equation Game Roots ±1 to ±6 Sheet 1

$$x^2-x-2=0$$

AIM

Quadratic Equation Game Roots ±1 to ±6 Sheet 1

$$x^2+5x+6=0$$

AIM

Quadratic Equation Game Roots ±1 to ±6 Sheet 1

$$x^2-4x+3=0$$

AIM

Quadratic Equation Game Roots ±1 to ±6 Sheet 1

$$x^2+3x+2=0$$

AIM

Quadratic Equation Game Roots ±1 to ±6 Sheet 1

$$x^2+5x+4=0$$

AIM

Quadratic Equation Game Roots ±1 to ±6 Sheet 1

$$x^2-8x+16=0$$

AIM

Quadratic Equation Game Roots ±1 to ±6 Sheet 1

$$x^2+8x+16=0$$

AIM

Quadratic Equation Game

Sheet 2

Roots ±1 to ±6

Quadratic Equation Game Roots ±1 to ±6 Sheet 2

$$x^2+2x+1=0$$

AIM

Quadratic Equation Game Roots ±1 to ±6 Sheet 2

$$x^2+6x+9=0$$

AIM

Quadratic Equation Game Roots ±1 to ±6 Sheet 2

$$x^2-7x+10=0$$

AIM

Quadratic Equation Game Roots ±1 to ±6 Sheet 2

$$x^2+x-12=0$$

AIM

Quadratic Equation Game Roots ±1 to ±6 Sheet 2

$$x^2-5x+6=0$$

AIM

Quadratic Equation Game Roots ±1 to ±6 Sheet 2

$$x^2+3x-10=0$$

AIM

Quadratic Equation Game Roots ±1 to ±6 Sheet 2

$$x^2+4x-5=0$$

AIM

Quadratic Equation Game Roots ±1 to ±6 Sheet 2

$$x^2-2x-15=0$$

AIM

Quadratic Equation Game Roots ±1 to ±6 Sheet 2

$$x^2+x-20=0$$

AIM

Quadratic Equation Game Roots ±1 to ±6 Sheet 2

$$x^2-3x-4=0$$

AIM

Quadratic Equation Game Roots ±1 to ±6 Sheet 2

$$x^2-2x-8=0$$

AIM

Quadratic Equation Game Roots ±1 to ±6 Sheet 2

$$x^2-7x+12=0$$

AIM

Quadratic Equation Game Roots ±1 to ±6 Sheet 2

$$x^2-8x+12=0$$

AIM

Quadratic Equation Game Roots ±1 to ±6 Sheet 2

$$x^2-9x+18=0$$

AIM

Quadratic Equation Game Roots ±1 to ±6 Sheet 2

$$x^2+3x-4=0$$

AIM

Quadratic Equation Game Roots ±1 to ±6 Sheet 2

$$x^2-8x+12=0$$

AIM

Quadratic Equation Game Roots ±1 to ±6 Sheet 2

$$x^2-25=0$$

AIM

Quadratic Equation Game Roots ±1 to ±6 Sheet 2

$$x^2-16=0$$

AIM

Simultaneous Equation Games

Introduction

Like the sequence games, these were developed to support a topic on simultaneous equations when I was doing research into games in school. The first three games develop the difficulty of the equations. The games are intended to allow the pupils to develop the techniques for solving simultaneous equations rather than providing practice. Thus the players should be left to find their own ways to solve the problems. The move to letters, which I explained by saying I was bored with thinking up pairs, or nonsense pairs, appeared not to cause any problems.

Match and Solve 4 is not part of this sequence of games, departing as it does from the linear equations. It is intended therefore to work on the idea of what it means to solve a pair of simultaneous equations rather than on techniques of solution.

Simultaneous Equation Game Rules

RULES FOR MATCH AND SOLVE GAMES

Players to play in pairs.

Place the cards face down on the table.

Each pair in turn turn over two cards. If the cards are clearly about the same problem, the players try to solve them. The rest of the group can help if necessary.

The cards are won by the pair who turn them up.

If the cards are not about the same problem then they are turned back and the next pair have a turn.

The pair with the most pairs win.

Note: the pairs in Match and Solve 4 are defined by the letter in the top right-hand side.

Match and Solve 1

Match and Solve 1

Two erasers and
a pencil cost 40p

ATM

Match and Solve 1

Two erasers and
3 pencils cost 60p

ATM

Match and Solve 1

A widgit and
3 bodgits cost 14p

ATM

Match and Solve 1

Three widgits
and 3 bodgits
cost 30p

ATM

Match and Solve 1

Three nails and
7 screws cost 27p

ATM

Match and Solve 1

Three nails and
4 screws cost 18p

ATM

Match and Solve 1

Two red stamps
and 4 blue
stamps cost 28p

ATM

Match and Solve 1

Two red stamps
and 1 blue
stamp cost 13p

ATM

Match and Solve 1

Six needles and
12 pins cost 30p

ATM

Match and Solve 1

Nine needles and
12 pins cost 39p

ATM

Match and Solve 1

Five blots and
3 snags cost 19p

ATM

Match and Solve 1

Five blots and
4 snags cost 22p

ATM

Match and Solve 1

Six wings and
2 wongs cost 70p

ATM

Match and Solve 1

Two wings and
2 wongs cost 34p

ATM

Match and Solve 1

Four chews and
1 lolly cost 41p

ATM

Match and Solve 1

Four chews and
9 lollies cost 113p

ATM

Match and Solve 1

Five zigs and
1 zag cost 22p

ATM

Match and Solve 1

Ten zigs and
1 zag cost 32p

ATM

Match and Solve 2

Match and Solve 2

Five erasers and
a pencil cost 20p

AIM

Match and Solve 2

Fifteen erasers and
two pencils cost 55p

AIM

Match and Solve 2

A widgit and
6 bodgits cost 33p

AIM

Match and Solve 2

Three nails and
2 screws cost 23p

AIM

Match and Solve 2

Six nails and
3 screws cost 42p

AIM

Match and Solve 2

Two widgits and
3 bodgits cost 21p

AIM

Match and Solve 2

Three red stamps
and 2 blue stamps
cost 13p

AIM

Match and Solve 2

One red stamp
and 3 blue stamps
cost 9p

AIM

Match and Solve 2

Three needles and
4 pins cost 17p

AIM

Match and Solve 2

Six blots and
2 snags cost 30p

AIM

Match and Solve 2

Twelve blots and
1 snag cost 51p

AIM

Match and Solve 2

Two needles and
a pin cost 8p

AIM

Match and Solve 2

Six wings and 5
wongs cost 43p

AIM

Match and Solve 2

Two chews and
1 lolly cost 13p

AIM

Match and Solve 2

One chew and
5 lollies cost 29p

AIM

Match and Solve 2

Three wings and
2 wongs cost 19p

AIM

Match and Solve 2

Five zigs and
2 zags cost 29p

AIM

Match and Solve 2

Ten zigs and
12 zags cost 74p

AIM

Match and Solve 3

Match and Solve 3

$$2A + 3B = 12$$

ATM

Match and Solve 3

$$2A + 5B = 16$$

ATM

Match and Solve 3

$$4C + D = 42$$

ATM

Match and Solve 3

$$5E + 5F = 35$$

ATM

Match and Solve 3

$$5E + 2F = 23$$

ATM

Match and Solve 3

$$6C + D = 58$$

ATM

Match and Solve 3

$$7G + 3H = 19$$

ATM

Match and Solve 3

$$10G + 3H = 22$$

ATM

Match and Solve 3

$$5J + 6K = 45$$

ATM

Match and Solve 3

$$6L + 9M = 60$$

ATM

Match and Solve 3

$$2L + 9M = 32$$

ATM

Match and Solve 3

$$5J + 10K = 65$$

ATM

Match and Solve 3

$$7N + 2P = 76$$

ATM

Match and Solve 3

$$7N + 7P = 91$$

ATM

Match and Solve 3

$$12Q + 3R = 30$$

ATM

Match and Solve 3

$$2W + 8T = 62$$

ATM

Match and Solve 3

$$10W + 8T = 86$$

ATM

Match and Solve 3

$$19Q + 3R = 37$$

ATM

Match and Solve 4

Match and Solve 4 **A**

$$\square + \Delta = 5$$

AIM

Match and Solve 4 **A**

$$\square - \Delta = 1$$

AIM

Match and Solve 4 **B**

$$\square + \Delta = 10$$

AIM

Match and Solve 4 **B**

$$\square - \Delta = 6$$

AIM

Match and Solve 4 **C**

$$\square + \Delta = 12$$

AIM

Match and Solve 4 **C**

$$\square \times \Delta = 20$$

AIM

Match and Solve 4 **D**

$$2\square + \Delta = 7$$

AIM

Match and Solve 4 **D**

$$\square + 2\Delta = 8$$

AIM

Match and Solve 4 **E**

$$\square + 1 = 7$$

AIM

Match and Solve 4 **E**

$$\Delta - 1 = 2\square$$

AIM

Match and Solve 4 **F**

$$\Delta - 3 = \square$$

AIM

Match and Solve 4 **F**

$$2\square = \Delta + 1$$

AIM

Match and Solve 4 **G**

$$2\square + 2\Delta = 12$$

AIM

Match and Solve 4 **G**

$$\square - \Delta = 2$$

AIM

Match and Solve 4 **H**

$$2\square - \Delta = 9$$

AIM

Match and Solve 4 **H**

$$2\Delta + 1 = 7$$

AIM

Match and Solve 4 **J**

$$3\square + 2\Delta = 8$$

AIM

Match and Solve 4 **J**

$$5\Delta - \square = 3$$

AIM

Sequence Games

Introduction

When I was developing these games in a school, I agreed to ensure that the group I was working with worked on the same topic as the rest of the class. I was unsure at first about what could be done with sequences but this set of games proved quite popular with the players.

The loop game establishes the notation for a sequence. The rule is that the value in the top left hand corner gives the term which must be calculated. So the card should be followed by a card with value 3.

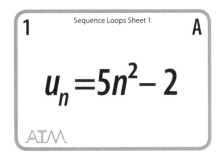

The other three games are concerned with arithmetic sequences, i.e. those with a constant difference between consecutive terms.

The longest sequence, with the variant way of calculating the score, can also be used in the sixth form when arithmetic sequences are studied in a more formal manner.

Create a Sequence

A GAME FOR 3 TO 4 PLAYERS.

Each player in turn throws a 0 to 9 dice twice. These two numbers in the **order in which they are thrown** are the first two terms of a sequence with a constant difference between the terms. If the two numbers are the same the player throws again.

For example if 3 and 7 are thrown the sequence is
   3, 7, 11, 15, ...

If 7 and 3 are thrown the sequence is
   7, 3, −1, −5, −9

The player scores the value of the sixth term.

The other players check the calculation.

Play continues until each player has had 10 turns. The winner is the player with the highest total of points.

Variant: The winner is the player with the lowest total of points.

Grab the Formula

A GAME FOR 3 TO 4 PLAYERS.

Each player in turn throws two 0 to 9 dice and arranges the numbers in ascending order. If the two numbers are the same the player throws again.

These two numbers are the first two terms of a sequence with a constant difference. The player writes down the next four terms of the sequence.

e.g. Throw 2 and 9

Player writes   2   9   16   23   30   37

The player then works out the formula for the nth term - in the example this is $7n - 5$.

The other players check the calculation and the formula. If it is correct and if no-one else has previously claimed this sequence, the player writes $7n - 5$ on his scorecard. If the formula has been claimed before then the formula cannot be claimed.

The player with the most formulae at the end wins.

Sequence Loops

8 · Sequence Loops Sheet 1 · A $$u_n = \dfrac{(n-6)^2}{4}$$ ATM	**1** · Sequence Loops Sheet 1 · A $$u_n = 5n^2 - 2$$ ATM	**3** · Sequence Loops Sheet 1 · A $$u_n = 2n^2 - 11$$ ATM
7 · Sequence Loops Sheet 1 · A $$u_n = \dfrac{n^2 - 1}{3}$$ ATM	**16** · Sequence Loops Sheet 1 · A $$u_n = \left(\dfrac{n}{4}\right)^2 - 11$$ ATM	**5** · Sequence Loops Sheet 1 · A $$u_n = \dfrac{n^2 - 1}{3}$$ ATM
3 · Sequence Loops Sheet 1 · B $$u_n = \dfrac{3n^2 + 3}{5}$$ ATM	**6** · Sequence Loops Sheet 1 · B $$u_n = \dfrac{n^2 - 1}{5}$$ ATM	**7** · Sequence Loops Sheet 1 · B $$u_n = (n-5)^2 + 1$$ ATM
5 · Sequence Loops Sheet 1 · B $$u_n = \dfrac{n^2 - 1}{6}$$ ATM	**4** · Sequence Loops Sheet 1 · B $$u_n = \dfrac{2n^2 - 8}{3}$$ ATM	**8** · Sequence Loops Sheet 1 · B $$u_n = \left(\dfrac{n}{4}\right)^2 - 1$$ ATM
3 · Sequence Loops Sheet 1 · C $$u_n = 2n^2 - 9$$ ATM	**9** · Sequence Loops Sheet 1 · C $$u_n = 6\left(\dfrac{n}{9}\right)^2$$ ATM	**6** · Sequence Loops Sheet 1 · C $$u_n = \dfrac{n^2}{9}$$ ATM
4 · Sequence Loops Sheet 1 · C $$u_n = n^2$$ ATM	**16** · Sequence Loops Sheet 1 · C $$u_n = \left(\dfrac{n}{8}\right)^2 + 4$$ ATM	**8** · Sequence Loops Sheet 1 · C $$u_n = 3\left(\dfrac{n}{8}\right)^2$$ ATM

Sequence Loops

2 Sequence Loops Sheet 2 · D $u_n = 3n^2 - 6$ ATM	**6** Sequence Loops Sheet 2 · D $u_n = \left(\dfrac{n}{2}\right)^2$ ATM	**9** Sequence Loops Sheet 2 · D $u_n = (n - 8)^2$ ATM
1 Sequence Loops Sheet 2 · D $u_n = 4n^2 - 1$ ATM	**3** Sequence Loops Sheet 2 · D $u_n = 2n^2 - 2$ ATM	**16** Sequence Loops Sheet 2 · D $u_n = \left(\dfrac{n}{8}\right)^2 - 2$ ATM
3 Sequence Loops Sheet 2 · E $u_n = n^2 - 7$ ATM	**2** Sequence Loops Sheet 2 · E $u_n = 2n^2$ ATM	**8** Sequence Loops Sheet 2 · E $u_n = \dfrac{n^2 - 1}{9}$ ATM
7 Sequence Loops Sheet 2 · E $u_n = (n - 4)^2$ ATM	**9** Sequence Loops Sheet 2 · E $u_n = \dfrac{n^2 - 1}{8}$ ATM	**10** Sequence Loops Sheet 2 · E $u_n = \left(\dfrac{n}{5}\right)^2 - 1$ ATM
3 Sequence Loops Sheet 2 · F $u_n = 2n^2 - 9$ ATM	**9** Sequence Loops Sheet 2 · F $u_n = \dfrac{n^2 + 19}{20}$ ATM	**5** Sequence Loops Sheet 2 · F $u_n = \dfrac{2n^2 + 10}{5}$ ATM
12 Sequence Loops Sheet 2 · F $u_n = \left(\dfrac{n}{4}\right)^2 - 2$ ATM	**7** Sequence Loops Sheet 2 · F $u_n = (n - 5)^2$ ATM	**4** Sequence Loops Sheet 2 · F $u_n = 2n^2 - 29$ ATM

The Longest Sequence

A GAME FOR 3 TO 4 PLAYERS.

You will need a pack of cards labelled 1 to 50 and an egg timer or a similar time measurer.

The players should agree how long each round will last.

Shuffle the cards and place them face down on the table.

In each round of the game the players draw two cards each.

Each player has to construct the longest possible sequence with a constant difference of 2 or more, starting with the smallest number and ending at the largest number.

For example if the numbers drawn are 5 and 26 the longest sequence possible is 5, 8, 11, 14, 17, 20, 23, 26.

This sequence has 8 terms and scores 8 points.

If the numbers were 7 and 36, the only sequence possible is 7, 36.

This sequence scores 2.

When time is up each player shows their sequence for checking and once it has been agreed records the points they have scored.

Variant : each player scores the total of the numbers in their sequence.

Assorted Games

Introduction

Running Total 1 and 2 are games designed to improve the fluency of pupils in handling algebraic expressions. They offer two different structures of a game in which the expression used could be changed to practise e.g. more or less complicated expressions, using any chosen letters or indeed quadratic expressions.

The Bingo game allows players to consider what values a particular expression can take for the values available on a dice.

The Yin Yang game seems to have the power to help children to develop their own rules for calculations with directed numbers, particularly if they are not given too large a supply of counters so that they become aware of the fact that they can add −5 rather than taking away 5 or take away −3 rather than adding 3. These strategies seem to develop naturally in the wake of the tactic of putting on pairs of red and black counters to make an operation possible. It is however important to stay with the image long enough for the link between it and the abstract to be well forged and to go back and forward between the two. In this way the procedural rules which are developed can be justified and the explanations retained.

Quadratic Dominoes is just what its title suggests. It does however work towards pupils being able to recognise the factors of simple quadratic expressions mentally - perhaps using the sum and product of the roots.

Running Total

Running Total 1

A game for the whole class or later for a group

Each player must write down an expression of the form $ax + b$ where neither a nor b is zero as their starting expression.

The teacher (or later the group) throws two dice.

The first dice is marked $-1, -2, -3, 1, 2, 3$.
The second dice is marked $+x, +2x, +3x, -x, -2x, -3x$.

Each throw of the dice produces an instruction to the players of the form :
    Add $2x$ and subtract 3.

This means that at each stage the player still holds an expression of the form $ax + b$.

Various forms of scoring are possible e.g.

- The player with the most/ least number of x at the end wins

- A player scores a point every time he reaches either ax or b

- A player scores a point whenever his expression has $a = b$

- Others that the pupils will invent!

Running Total 2

In this version of the game, each 'player' (could be a pair) chooses an expression of the form $ax + by$ where neither a nor b is zero. They display their expression at all times so that other players can see what it is.

Each player in turn throws a standard dice and gives the instruction to everyone to add or subtract this number of xs or ys.

If any player's total is zero then they score 2, if their expression contains either no xs or no ys they score 1.

Before the game starts define a checking mechanism e.g. play individually but identify pairs who check for each other.

Substitution Bingo

Shufffle the set of expression cards and put them face down on the table.

Every player creates a bingo card on squared paper.

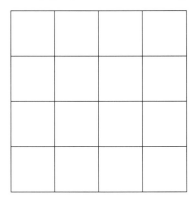

Turn up the top card. This is the expression to be used for the first round.

The players then write 12 different numbers in their bingo card. Obviously the choice of numbers can be tailored to the expression turned up. For some expressions players may choose negative numbers.

Two (1-6) dice of different colours are then rolled, one to represent the value of a and one the value of b. Students substitute these values in and cross off the matching value on their card. The winner can be either the first player to complete a row/column or the first to complete the whole card.

This can also be played as a whole class game, with the teacher choosing the expression for each round.

Expressions for Bingo

Expressions for Bingo

$a + b$

Expressions for Bingo

$2a + b$

Expressions for Bingo

$2a - b$

Expressions for Bingo

$a + 3b$

Expressions for Bingo

$4b - a$

Expressions for Bingo

$a^2 + b$

Expressions for Bingo

$a^2 - b$

Expressions for Bingo

$a^2 + b^2$

Expressions for Bingo

$2(b - a)$

Expressions for Bingo

$2(b + a)$

Expressions for Bingo

$2(b - a)$

Expressions for Bingo

$4(b + a)$

Expressions for Bingo

$2(a^2 + b^2)$

Expressions for Bingo

$2(a^2 - b^2)$

Expressions for Bingo

$5a - b$

Expressions for Bingo

$4a + b$

Expressions for Bingo

$5b - a$

Expressions for Bingo

$$\frac{a + b}{2}$$

The Yin Yang Game

In this game negative and positive numbers are represented by collections of red and black counters. The black counters are positive and the red counters negative.

A number can be created in more then one way:

2 can be represented by

> 2 black counters
> *or*
> by 3 black counters and a red counter
> *or*
> 4 black counters and 2 red counters and so on.

−3 can be represented by

> 3 red counters
> *or*
> by 4 red counters and a black counter
> *or*
> 5 red counters and 2 black counters etc.

You need a 1 to 6 dice, a +/− dice and a blank dice marked *Add* and *Subtract* three times each.

The game starts by one player throwing the 1 to 6 dice and the +/− dice to establish a starting number. This can then be represented in any way the player likes. The number thrown is the player's first score.

Subsequent turns consist of throwing all three dice and carrying out the instruction by adding or removing counters of one colour only. In order to achieve a removal any equal number of counters of both colours may be added to change the representation of the number before the operation is carried out.

So if the current total is 3 and is represented by 4 blacks and 1 red and the player is required to subtract −5, 4 red and 4 black cubes must be added to make the move possible. The player scores the total shown by the counters when the turn has finished.

At the end of the game the players total their scores and the highest (or lowest) total wins.

Quadratic Dominoes Rules

A co-operative or competitive game for 2 to 4 players.

To start with this game can be played as a co-operative game with the group of pupils attempting to arrange the dominoes in a long line. As they develop greater fluency it can be played as a competitive game.

Two dominoes can be placed together if they share a linear factor, so

$x^2 - 3x + 2$ and $x^2 - x - 2$

can be placed next to each other since they share a factor of $x - 2$.

Dominoes are played in the usual way with each player starting with 7 dominoes and picking up from the remaining pile if they cannot go.

It may be valuable to play with the dominoes face up on the table so that players can help each other as needed. This also introduces a valuable element of strategy if a player has a choice of cards to play.

Quadratic Dominoes

Quadratic Dominoes Sheet 1

$x^2 + 4x - 32$

ATM

Quadratic Dominoes Sheet 1

$x^2 - 10x + 16$

ATM

Quadratic Dominoes Sheet 1

$x^2 - x - 6$

ATM

Quadratic Dominoes Sheet 1

$x^2 - 2x - 3$

ATM

Quadratic Dominoes Sheet 1

$x^2 - 3x + 2$

ATM

Quadratic Dominoes Sheet 1

$x^2 - 2x - 8$

ATM

Quadratic Dominoes Sheet 1

$x^2 + 7x + 12$

ATM

Quadratic Dominoes Sheet 1

$x^2 - 2x - 15$

ATM

Quadratic Dominoes Sheet 1

$x^2 + 4x - 5$

ATM

Quadratic Dominoes Sheet 1

$x^2 - 13x + 40$

ATM

Quadratic Dominoes Sheet 1

$x^2 - 9x + 8$

ATM

Quadratic Dominoes Sheet 1

$x^2 - x - 2$

ATM

Quadratic Dominoes Sheet 1

$x^2 + 5x + 6$

ATM

Quadratic Dominoes Sheet 1

$x^2 + 4x + 3$

ATM

Quadratic Dominoes Sheet 1

$x^2 + 3x + 2$

ATM

Quadratic Dominoes Sheet 1

$x^2 + 5x + 4$

ATM

Quadratic Dominoes Sheet 1

$x^2 + 11x + 28$

ATM

Quadratic Dominoes Sheet 1

$x^2 + 6x - 7$

ATM

Quadratic Dominoes

Quadratic Dominoes Sheet 2

$$x^2 + 5x - 14$$

ATM

Quadratic Dominoes Sheet 2

$$x^2 + 4x - 21$$

ATM

Quadratic Dominoes Sheet 2

$$x^2 - 11x + 24$$

ATM

Quadratic Dominoes Sheet 2

$$x^2 + x - 12$$

ATM

Quadratic Dominoes Sheet 2

$$x^2 - 5x + 6$$

ATM

Quadratic Dominoes Sheet 2

$$x^2 + 3x - 10$$

ATM

Quadratic Dominoes Sheet 2

$$x^2 + 4x - 5$$

ATM

Quadratic Dominoes Sheet 2

$$x^2 + 2x - 15$$

ATM

Quadratic Dominoes Sheet 2

$$x^2 + x - 20$$

ATM

Quadratic Dominoes Sheet 2

$$x^2 - 3x - 4$$

ATM

Quadratic Dominoes Sheet 2

$$x^2 - 2x - 8$$

ATM

Quadratic Dominoes Sheet 2

$$x^2 - 7x + 12$$

ATM

Quadratic Dominoes Sheet 2

$$x^2 - 10x + 24$$

ATM

Quadratic Dominoes Sheet 2

$$x^2 - 5x - 6$$

ATM

Quadratic Dominoes Sheet 2

$$x^2 - 7x + 6$$

ATM

Quadratic Dominoes Sheet 2

$$x^2 - 13x + 42$$

ATM

Quadratic Dominoes Sheet 2

$$x^2 - 11x + 28$$

ATM

Quadratic Dominoes Sheet 2

$$x^2 - 6x - 7$$

ATM